WITHDRAWN

COCK-A-DOODLE DANDY

COCK-A-DOODLE DANDY

BY

SEAN O'CASEY

LONDON

MACMILLAN & CO. LTD

1949

TO

JAMES STEPHENS

THE JESTING POET
WITH A RADIANT STAR
IN'S COXCOMB

CHARACTERS IN THE PLAY

THE COCK

MICHAEL MARTHRAUN. *A small farmer, now the owner of a lucrative bog*

SAILOR MAHAN. *Once a sailor, now the owner of a fleet of lorries carrying turf from bog to town*

LORNA. *Second young wife of Marthraun*

LORELEEN. *Marthraun's daughter by his first young wife*

MARION. *Helper in Lorna's house*

SHANAAR. *A " very wise old crawthumper ", really a dangerous old cod*

1ST ROUGH FELLOW ⎫ *Peasants working on the bog*
2ND ROUGH FELLOW ⎭

FATHER DOMINEER. *The parish priest of Nyadnanave*

THE SERGEANT. *Of the Civic Guard*

JACK. *Mahan's foreman lorry driver*

JULIA. *Lorna's sister, a paralytic on a visit to Lourdes*

HER FATHER

ONE-EYED LARRY. *A peasant lad and potential sacristan*

A MAYOR

A MACE-BEARER

THE MESSENGER. *In love with Marion*

THE BELLMAN. *A kind of town crier*

A PORTER. *Of a general store in the near-by town*

v

SCENES

SCENE I

Part of the garden outside the house of Michael Marthraun. It is rough and uncared-for, with tough grass everywhere, sprinkled with buttercups and daisies. It is surrounded by a stone wall, three to four feet high, which is pierced by a wooden gate to the right of any visitor entering the garden. To the left, a little way from the gate, a clump of sunflowers, in full bloom, stand stiff and stately, their blossoms big as shields, the petals raying out widely and sharply, like rays from an angry sun. Glancing farther to the left, a visitor would see the gable-end of the house, with a porch jutting from it, and a window above the porch. The porch is supported by twisted pillars of wood, looking like snakes, which are connected with lattice-work shaped like noughts and crosses. These are painted a dazzling white. The frame-work of the window above is a little on the skew, and the sash-work holding the glass is twisted into irregular lines. A little way from the porch, towards the wall, is a dignified-looking bronze urn holding a stand-offish, cynical-looking evergreen. Farther up, near the wall, the Irish Tricolour flutters from a flag-pole. The house itself is black in colour, the sash and frame of the window in it is a brilliant red.

It is a brilliantly fine day in summer, and as there is nothing in the garden to provide a shade, the place is a deep pool of heat, which, seemingly, has lasted for some time, for the grass has turned to a deep yellow hue, save where the house and porch throw a rich black shadow. Stretching away in the distance, beyond the wall, is a bog of a rich purple colour, dabbed here and there with black patches. The sky above it is a silvery grey, glittering like an oriental canopy.

Some little distance away, an accordion is heard playing a

I

dance tune, and, a few moments after, the Cock comes dancing in around the gable of the house, circles the dignified urn, and disappears round the farther end of the gable-end as the music ceases.

He is of a deep black plumage, fitted to his agile and slender body like a glove on a lady's hand ; yellow feet and ankles, bright-green flaps like wings, and a stiff cloak falling like a tail behind him. A big crimson crest flowers over his head, and crimson flaps hang from his jaws. His face has the look of a cynical jester.

Michael Marthraun, followed by Sailor Mahan, comes into the garden by the porch. Each carries a kitchen chair, which they set down some way from the house. Michael is a man who is well over sixty years of age, clean-shaven, lean, and grim-looking. His lips twitch nervously whenever he forgets to keep his mouth tightly closed. He is dressed in a blackish tweed suit, and his legs are encased in black leggings. A heavy gold chain stretches across his waistcoat, and he wears a wide-leafed collar, under which a prim black bow is tied.

Sailor Mahan is a little over fifty, stouter than his companion, and of a more serene countenance. He has a short, pointed beard, just beginning to show signs of greyness. His face is of a ruddier hue, and shows that the wind and the stress of many storms have made it rugged, but in no way unpleasant. There is, maybe, a touch of the sea-breeze in his way of talking and his way of walking. He is wearing light-grey flannel trousers, a double-breasted royal blue coat, and has a white scarf round his neck, over a light-blue shirt. They come to the two chairs, and stand there facing each other.

Michael. Come out here, come on out here, where a body can talk free. There's whispers an' whispers in that house, upsettin' a man's mind.

Mahan [*puzzled*]. Whispers ? What kinda whispers ?

Michael. Sthrange kinds ; whispers good for neither soul nor body.

Mahan. But there's no-one in the house but your wife, Lorna, Marion the maid, and your own girl Loreleen ?

Michael. Ay, so you think ; but I know different.

Mahan [*breezily*]. Nonsense, Mick ; you're haulin' on a rope that isn't there !

Michael [*raising his voice*]. You don't live in th' house, do you ? [*Mahan is silent.*] You don't live in th' house, do you ?

Mahan [*raising his voice too*]. I know I don't live in it, an' if it's like what you say, I don't want to live in it !

Michael. Well then, keep quiet when a man speaks of what he knows.

Mahan. I know as much about a whisper as you do.

Michael. You know about th' whispers of wind an' wave, harmless an' innocent things ; but I'm talkin' about whispers ebbin' an' flowin' about th' house, with an edge of evil on them, since that painted one, that godless an' laughin' little bitch left London to come here for a long an' leering holiday.

Mahan. Loreleen ? Why, man, she's your own daughter by your first young wife !

Michael. So it was said at th' time, an' so it's believed still ; but I had me doubts then, and I've more doubts now. I dhread meetin' her, dhread it, dhread it. [*With a frightened laugh*] Michael Marthraun's daughter ! [*Gripping Mahan's arm*] Is she anyone's daughter, man ?

Mahan [*impatiently*]. She must be somebody's daughter, man !

Michael [*impatiently*]. Why must she be, man ? Remember what th' Missioner said last night : Sthrange things are foisted by the powers of evil into th' life o' man. Since that one come back from England, where evil things abound, there's sinisther signs appearin' everywhere, evil evocations floatin' through every room.

Mahan [*puzzled*]. What kinda evocation an' significality is there ?

Michael [*looking suspiciously at the porch, then at the window above it, and drawing Mahan farther away from the house*]. Looka, Sailor Mahan [*he speaks furtively*] there's always a stern commotion among th' holy objects of th' house, when that one, Loreleen, goes sailin' by ; an invisible wind blows th' pictures out, an' turns their frenzied faces to th' wall ; once I seen the statue of St. Crankarius standin' on his head to circumvent th' lurin' quality of her presence ; an' another time, I seen th' image of our own St. Pathrick makin' a skelp at her with his crozier ; fallin' flat on his face, stunned, when he missed !

Mahan [*doubtful, but a little impressed*]. Good God, them's serious things, Michael Marthraun ! [*A pause.*] Are you sure, now, Mick, you're not deludin' yourself ?

Michael. Have sense, man ! An' me own wife, Lorna Marthraun, is mixin' herself with th' disordher, fondlin' herself with all sorts o' dismayin' decorations. Th' other day, I caught her gapin' into a lookin'-glass, an' when I looked meself, I seen gay-coloured horns branchin' from her head !

Mahan. No ! Oh, Mick, you're fancyin' things. Lorna's a fine, upstandin' woman. an' should be respected.

Michael. Are you gone on her, too ? I tell you, I seen the way th' eyes of young men stare at her face, an' follow th' movements of her lurin' legs — there's evil in that woman !

Mahan. But there's nothin' evil in a pretty face, or in a pair of lurin' legs.

Michael. Oh, man, your religion should tell you th' biggest fight th' holy saints ever had was with temptations from good-lookin' women.

Mahan [*getting nervous, and eager to change the subject*]. Looka, let's sit down, an' thry to settle about what you're willin' to pay for th' cartage of th' turf.

Michael [*ignoring Mahan's attempt to change the tide of talk*]. Up there in that room [*he points to the window above the porch*] she often dances be herself, but dancin' in her mind with hefty lads, plum'd with youth, an' spurred with looser thoughts of love. [*As he speaks, the sounds of a gentle waltz are heard, played by harp, lute, or violin, or by all three, the sounds coming, apparently, from the room whose window is above the porch. Bitterly*] There, d'ye hear that, man ! Mockin' me. She'll hurt her soul, if she isn't careful.

Mahan. She's young enough yet to nourish th' need o' dancin'. An' anyway, why did you insist on marryin' her, an' she so young ; an' she so gay ? She was all again' it herself.

Michael. She consented to it, at last, didn't she ?

Mahan. Ay, when you, her father, an' th' priest had

badgered th' girl's mind into disordered attention over th' catch she was gettin'.

Michael. Oh, well you know, Sailor Mahan, that she had her blue eye on th' fat little farm undher me feet ; th' taut roof over me head ; an' th' kind cushion I had in th' bank, against a hard day.

Mahan. I seen you meself throtting afther her from starboard to port, from poop to quarther-deck, hoistin' before her th' fancy of ribbon an' lace, silver-buckled shoes, an' a silk dhress for Sunday.

Michael. An' what had she but a patched petticoat, a worn look, an' broken brogues to wear to Mass on Sundays ? An' didn't I give her oul' fella fifty solid pounds so that her ailin' sisther could thravel to Lourdes to get undher th' aegis of th' Blessed Virgin ? An' what did I get for them but a scraggy oul' bog of two hundhred acres ?

Mahan. An' you're makin a good thing out of it since turf came into its own. It's made you a Councillor, a Justice of th' Peace, an' th' fair-haired boy of th' clergy.

Michael. As you mentioned turf, we'd betther settle this question of you demandin', for carting it, an exthra amount I couldn't possibly pay.

Mahan [*stiffness coming into his voice*]. You'll have to, Michael Marthraun, for it can't be done now for a cent less.

Michael. We'll have a drink while we're discussin'. I have a bottle of th' best, ten years maturin', inside. Sit down there till I get it. [*He goes into the porch and, after a few moments, comes quickly out again, his mouth twitching, his voice toned to fear and hate.*] That one, Loreleen's comin' down th' stairs, an' I don't want to come too near her. We'll wait till she goes. Let's talk of our affairs, quietly, while she passes by. Th' thing to do, as Shanaar would tell you, when you hear a sound or see a shape of anything evil, is to take no notice of it. [*Whispering impatiently*] Sit down, man !

Mahan [*sitting down — dubiously*]. Are you sure, Mick, you have a close-hauled comprehension of th' way you're thinkin' ?

Michael. Ay, am I sure ; as sure as I am that a cock crows !

> [*A cock suddenly crows lustily as Loreleen appears in the doorway of the porch. She is a very attractive young woman with an air of her own. A jaunty air it is, indicating that it is the sign of a handsome, gay, and intelligent woman. She is dressed in a darkish green dress, with dark-red flashes on bodice and side of skirt. A saucy hat of a brighter green than the dress sports a scarlet ornament, its shape suggestive of a cock's crimson crest. Her legs — very charming ones — are clad in brown silk stockings ; brown that flashes a golden sheen.*
>
> [*Michael, who has sat down, jumps startled to his feet at the sudden sound of the cock's crow and, stretching over the table, grips Mahan by the shoulder.*

Michael. What's that, what's that ?

Mahan [*startled by Michael's frightened movement*]. What's what, man ?

Michael [*trying to recover himself*]. Nothin', I heard nothin'. What was it you were sayin' ? [*In a whisper*] Get goin' on th' turf, man.

Mahan [*mystified, but doing his best*]. You'll have to grant
th' two shillin's additional on each load, Mick. I'd
work me lorries at a loss if I took less. [*Placing an
affectionate hand on Michael's shoulder*] An' you know well,
you're such an oul' an' valued friend, I'd do it for
affection's sake, if I only could.

Michael [*forgetting about Loreleen*]. Don't I know that well,
Sailor Mahan ; an' I'd do th' same, an' more, be you ;
but if I surrendhered two shillin's, I might as well
give you th' bog as well. I have to live, Sailor Mahan.

Mahan. Damn it, man, haven't I to live too ? How th'
hell am I goin' to give th' men a shillin' more without
th' exthra two shillin's from you ? Pray to th' saints
to let them fall like rain from heaven, eh ?

Michael [*putting his face closer to Mahan's, hotly*]. Looka here,
Sailor Mahan, you're not goin' to magicfy me into th'
dhream of believin' you're not addin', every hurryin'
week, a fine bundle o' notes to th' jubilant store you've
there already, forcin' overtime on th' poor men o' th'
bank, flickin' th' notes into imperial ordher.

Mahan [*as fiercely — standing up to say it, his face close to the
face of Michael*]. An' you yourself, Michael Marthraun,
aren't worn away with th' punishment of poverty !
Puttin' on a poor mouth, an' if you set out to count
graciously all you have in hidlins, you'd be workin'
many a long, glad day, without supper or sleep, be day-
light an' candle-light, till your mind centhred on th'
sum dominated be th' last note fluttherin' from your
fingers !

Loreleen [*who has strolled slowly over to the gate, listening to the
talk the while, turning at the gate to watch as well as listen*].

Lay not up for yourselves treasures upon earth, where moth and rust doth corrupt, and where thieves break through and steal !

Michael [*in a frightened whisper*]. Don't turn your head ; take no notice. Don't pretend to hear her lyin' hallucinations !

> [*A young, rough-looking Fellow, well-set and strong, comes running along the pathway to the gate. He is wearing dark-brown corduroy trousers, belted at waist, grey shirt, and scarf of bright green, with yellow dots. He pushes Loreleen aside.*

1st Rough Fellow [*pushing Loreleen out of his way*]. Outa me way, woman ! [*He sees how charming she is as he swings her aside.*] Be God, but you're th' good-lookin' lass ! What are you doin' in this hole ?

Loreleen. Seeking happiness, an' failing to find it.

1st Rough Fellow. It isn't here you should be, lost among th' rough stones, th' twisty grass, an' th' moody misery of th' brown bog ; but it's lyin' laughin' you should be where th' palms are tall, an' wherever a foot is planted, a scarlet flower is crushed ; where there's levity living its life, an' not loneliness dyin' as it is here.

Loreleen [*dropping him a deep curtsy*]. Thank you, sir knight, for th' silken compliments to your handmaiden.

> [*She turns to go out, and the Rough Fellow hurries in through the gate, down to the two men.*

1st Rough Fellow [*going through the gate down to where the two men are, and turning to speak up to Loreleen, still standing at the gate*]. If you wait till I'm done with these fellas [*he indicates Michael and Mahan*] I could go to th' bend o' th'

road with you, for it's meself would surrendher a long
spell of heaven's ease to go a long day's journey with a
lass like you !

> [*Another Rough Fellow hurries in along the pathway out-
> side to the gate, pulling Loreleen aside when he finds her in
> his way. He wears light-brown corduroy trousers, check
> shirt, and has a scarf of light yellow, with green stripes,
> round his neck.*

2nd Rough Fellow [*pulling Loreleen out of his way*]. Eh, there,
woman — outa me way ! [*He sees, as she swings around,
how charming she is.*] Arra, what winsome wind blew
such a flower into this dread, dhried-up desert ? Deirdre
come to life again, not to sorrow, but to dance ! If Eve
was as you are, no wondher Adam fell, for a lass like
you could shutther th' world away with a kiss !

> [*He goes through the gate, and down to the other men,
> pausing to look up at Loreleen again.*

2nd Rough Fellow [*to Loreleen*]. Wait, lass, till I'm done
with these fellas, an' I'll go with you till youth's a
shadow a long way left behind !

Loreleen [*down to the two Rough Fellows*]. I'm not for you,
friends, for I'm not good for decent men. The two old
cronies will tell you a kiss from me must be taken
undher a canopy of dangerous darkness. [*She kisses a
hand to them.*] Goodbye !

> [*She goes out.*

Michael⎱ [*together*]. What d'ye th' two of yous want here ?
Mahan⎰ Why aren't yous at work ?

1st Rough Fellow [*laying a hand sternly on the shoulder of
Mahan*]. Looka, you ; you give us th' exthra shillin', or

we leave your lorries standin', helpless an' naked on th' roads !

2nd Rough Fellow [*laying a hand sternly on Michael's shoulder*]. Looka, you ; looka that ! [*He throws a cheque contemptuously on to the table.*] D'ye think a good week's wages is in a cheque for tuppence ?

Michael. You didn't work a week, because of th' rain, an' canteen contribution an' insurance brought your wage for the week to tuppence.

2nd Rough Fellow. Tell me how I'm goin' to live a week on tuppence ?

1st Rough Fellow. Seein' th' both of them's knights o' Columbanus, they should be able to say.

Michael. That's a social question to be solved by th' Rerum Novarum.

2nd Rough Fellow. Fifty years old ; not worth much when it was born, an' not worth a damn now. You give a guaranteed week, or th' men come off your bog !

[*He goes off towards the gate.*

1st Rough Fellow [*going to the gate — to Mahan*]. Take our demand serious, or your lorries stand still on th' highways !

2nd Rough Fellow [*impatiently*]. Looka, there she is ! [*He points a finger in front.*] Let's hurry, an' we'll ketch up on th' fine, fair lady.

[*They hurry along the path, but suddenly stop to stare ahead.*

1st Rough Fellow [*with awe in his voice*]. What's happenin' to her ? A cloud closin' in on her, flashes like lightning whirlin' round her head, an' her whole figure ripplin' !

B

2nd Rough Fellow [*frightened*]. Jasus, she's changin' into th' look of a fancy-bred fowl ! It's turnin' to face us ; it's openin' its bake as big as a bayonet !

[*The crow of a cock is heard in the distance.*]

1st Rough Fellow [*frightened*]. Here, man, th' other way for us ! It's an omen, a warnin', a reminder of what th' Missioner said last night that young men should think of good-lookin' things in skirts only in th' presence of, an' undher th' guidance of, old and pious people.

[*The two of them hurry away in the opposite direction.*]

Michael [*to Mahan*]. Did you hear that ? I'm askin' you, Sailor Mahan, did you hear what them two graspin' rascals said ?

Mahan. I heard, but I can see no significality in it, unless th' two of them had dhrink taken.

Michael [*warningly*]. Looka, Sailor Mahan, if you aren't careful, your wilful disbelief in things'll lead you asthray ! Loreleen isn't me daughter ; she isn't even a woman : she's either undher a spell, or she's a possessed person.

Mahan [*with contempt*]. Aw, for God's sake, Mick, have sense, an' get that bottle o' whiskey out to put a spell on us.

Michael [*almost shouting*]. Have you forgotten already th' case of th' Widow Malone who could turn, twinklin', into a dog or a hare, when she wanted to hide herself ? An' how, one day, th' dogs followed what they thought was a hare that made for th' widow's cottage, an' dived through an open window, one o' th' dogs snappin' a leg off before it could get through. An' when th' door was burst open, there was th' oul' witch-widow screamin' on her oul' bed, one leg gone, with blood spoutin' from th' stump, so that all th' people heard her last screechin' as she went sliddherin' down to hell!

Mahan. I heard tell of it months after, when I come back from Valparaiso.

Michael. Well, if you heard of it, you know it must have happened. An' here you are, thinkin' only of whiskey, and showin' how ready you are to ruin me be askin' more than I'm able to give. You, a good Christian, a knight of St. Columbanus, a student in th' Circle studyin' th' Rerum Novarum, you should show a sign of charity an' justice, recognisin' th' needs of th' people rather than your own. [*Suddenly*] Here, I'll add thruppence, an' make th' offer ninepence. Hold out th' hand, an' clinch th' bargain.

Mahan. I'll be scuppered if I will! You'll not use me like th' oul' father of th' good woman within, who sold you th' bog when he thought it was derelict, though you're makin' thousands out of it now.

Michael. You forget I gave th' oul' cod enough to bring his other daughter to Lourdes for a cure!

Mahan. You know th' way th' men are actin' now — goin' slow, an' doin' two journeys where they used to do three.

Michael. An' aren't my men threatenin' to come off th' bog altogether? It's this materialism's doin' it — edgin' into revolt against Christian conduct. If they'd only judge o' things in th' proper Christian way, as we do, there'd be no disputes. Now let's be good sons of

Columbanus — you thinkin' of my difficulties, an' me thinkin' of yours.

Mahan. Make your offer one an' sixpence, an' I'll hoist th' pennant of agreement ?

Michael. I couldn't. Looka, Sailor Mahan, it would ruin me.

Mahan [*viciously*]. You'd rather throw th' money after a tall-hat so that you could controvert yourself into a dapper disturbance th' time the president comes to view th' workin' of th' turf. Talk about Loreleen castin' a spell ! Th' whole disthrict'll be paralysed in a spell when your top-hat comes out to meet the president's top-hat, th' two poor things tryin' to keep people from noticin' what's undher them ! Two shillin's, now, or nothin'. [*He sits down in disgust.*

[*Behind the wall, Shanaar is seen coming along the road ; he opens the gate, and comes slowly down to where the two men are. He is a very, very old man, wrinkled like a walnut, bent at the shoulders, with longish white hair, and a white beard — a bit dirty — reaching to his belly. He is dressed peasant-wise, thin, threadbare frieze coat, patched blackish corduroy trousers, thick boots, good and strong, a vivid blue muffler round his neck, and a sackcloth waistcoat, on which hangs a brass cross, suspended round his neck by twine. A round, wide-brimmed, black hat is on his head.*

Shanaar [*lifting his hat as he comes in by the gate*]. God save all here ! God save all that may be in th' house, barrin' th' cat an' th' dog !

Michael [*with great respect*]. An' you, too, Shanaar, old, old man, full of wisdom an' th' knowledge of deeper things.

Shanaar. Old is it? Ever so old, thousands of years, thousands of years if all were told.

Michael. Me an' Sailor Mahan here were talkin' some time ago, about th' sthrange dodges of unseen powers, an' of what the Missioner said about them last night, but th' easiness of his mind hasn't been hindhered.

Shanaar [*bending lower, and shoving his bearded face between the two men*]. If it doesn't hindher th' easiness of his mind now, it will one day! Maybe this very day in this very place.

Michael [*to Mahan*]. What d'ye say to that, now?

Mahan [*trying to be firm, but a little uneasy*]. Nothin', nothin'.

Shanaar [*shoving his face closer to Mahan's*]. Ah, me friend, for years an' years I've thravelled over hollow lands an' hilly lands, an' I know. Big powers of evil, with their little powers, an' them with their littler ones, an' them with their littlest ones, are everywhere. You might meet a bee that wasn't a bee; a bird that wasn't a bird; or a beautiful woman who wasn't a woman at all.

Michael [*excitedly*]. I'm tellin' him that, I'm tellin' him that all along!

Mahan [*a little doubtfully — to Shanaar*]. An' how's a poor body to know them?

Shanaar [*looking round cautiously, then speaking in a tense whisper*]. A sure sign, if only you can get an all-round glimpse of them. [*He looks round him again.*] *Daemones posteriora non habent* — they have no behinds !

Michael [*frightened a lot*]. My God, what an awe-inspiring, expiring experience !

Mahan [*frightened too, but trying to appear brave*]. That may be, but I wouldn't put innocent birds or bees in that category.

Shanaar [*full of pitying scorn for ignorance*]. You wouldn't ! Innocent birds ! Listen all : There was a cuckoo once that led a holy brother to damnation. Th' cuckoo's call enticed th' brother to a silent glade where th' poor man saw a lovely woman, near naked, bathin' her legs in a pool, an' in an instant th' holy man was taken with desire. Lost ! She told him he was handsome, but he must have money if he wanted to get her. Th' brother entered a noble's house, an' demanded a hundhred crowns for his convent ; but the noble was a wise old bird, an' said he'd have to see the prior first. Thereupon, th' brother up with an axe, hidden undher his gown, an' cleft th' noble from skull to chin ; robbed th' noble, dhressed himself in rare velvets, an' searched out all th' rosy rottenness of sin with th' damsel till th' money was gone. Then they caught him. Then they hanged him, an', mind you [*the three heads come closer together*], while this poor brother sobbed on the scaffold, everyone heard th' mocking laughter of a girl and th' calling of a cuckoo !

[*As Shanaar is speaking the three last things, the mocking laughter of a girl is heard, the call of a cuckoo, and a young man's sobbing, one after the other, at first, then they blend together for a few moments, and cease. Shanaar stands as stiff as his bent back will allow, and the other*

*two rise slowly from their chairs, stiff, too, and
frightened.*

Shanaar [*in a tense whisper*]. Say nothing ; take no notice.
Sit down. Thry to continue as if yous hadn't heard !

Mahan [*after a pause*]. Ay, a cuckoo, maybe ; but that's a
foreign bird : no set harbour or home. No genuine
decent Irish bird would do a thing like that on a man.

Michael. Looka here, Sailor Mahan, when th' powers of
evil get goin', I wouldn't put anything past an ordinary
hen !

Shanaar. An' you'd be right, Mr. Marthraun, though, as
a rule, hens is always undher th' eye an' comprehension
of a Christian. Innocent-looking things are often th'
most dangerous. Looka th' lad whose mother had set
her heart on him bein' a priest, an' one day, at home, he
suddenly saw a corncrake flyin' into a house be an
open window. Climbin' in afther it, he spied a glittherin'
brooch on a table, an' couldn't resist th' temptation o'
thievin' it. That lad spent th' next ten years in a
reformatory ; his mother died of a broken heart, and
his father took to dhrink.

[*During the recital of Shanaar's story, the " crek crek, crek
crek" of a corncrake is heard.*

Michael [*in a tense whisper — to Mahan*]. D'ye hear that,
Sailor Mahan ?

Shanaar [*warningly*]. Hush ! Take no vocal notice.
When yous hear anything or see anything suspicious,
give it no notice, unless you know how to deal with it.

Michael [*solemnly*]. A warnin' we'll remember. But
supposin' a hen goes wrong, what are we to do ?

Shanaar [*thoughtfully*]. It isn't aysay to say, an' you have to go cautious. The one thing to do, if yous have the knowledge, is to parley with th' hens in a Latin dissertation. If among th' fowl there's an illusion of a hen from Gehenna, it won't endure th' Latin. She can't face th' Latin. Th' Latin downs her. She tangles herself in a helluva disordher. She busts asundher, an' disappears in a quick column of black an' blue smoke, a thrue ear ketchin' a screech of agony from its centre !

Michael [*tremendously impressed*]. Looka that now. See what it is to know ! [*A commotion is heard within the house : a loud cackling, mingled with a short sharpened crow of a cock ; the breaking of delf ; the half-angry, half-frightened cries of women. A cup, followed by a saucer, flies out through the open window, over the porch, past the heads of the three men, who duck violently, and then crouch, amazed, and a little frightened.*] What th' hell's happenin' now ?

[*Marion rushes to the door of the porch, frightened and alarmed. She is a young girl of twenty or so, and very good-looking. Her skirts come just to her knees, for they are nice legs, and she likes to show them — and why shouldn't she ? And when she does so, she can add the spice of a saucy look to her bright blue eyes. Instead of the usual maid's cap, she wears a scarf-bandeau round her head, ornamented with silver strips, joined in the centre above her forehead, with an enamelled stone, each strip extending along the bandeau as far as either ear. She wears a dark-green uniform, flashed with a brighter green on the sleeves and neck, and the buttons of the bodice are of the same colour. Her stockings and shoes are black. A small, neat, white apron, piped with green, protects her uniform.*]

Marion [*excitedly — to the men*]. It's flyin' about th' house, an' behavin' outrageous ! I guessed that that Loreleen's cluck, cluck, cluckin' would upset th' birds' respectable way of livin' !

Michael [*frightened*]. What's wrong with you, girl ; what's up ?

Marion. Will one of yous come in, an' ketch it, for God's sake, before it ruins th' house ?

Mahan [*shouting*]. Ketch what, ketch what, woman ?

Marion. A wild-goose ! It's sent th' althar light flyin' ; it's clawed the holy pictures ; an' now it's peckin' at th' tall-hat !

- *Michael*. A wild-goose ? Are you sure it was a wild one ?

Marion [*in great distress*]. I dunno, I dunno — maybe it's a wild-duck. It's some flyin' thing tearin' th' house asundher.

Michael [*trembling — to Shanaar*]. D'ye think it might be what you know ?

Shanaar [*his knees shaking a little*]. It might be, Mr. Marthraun ! it might be, God help us !

Mahan [*nervous himself*]. Keep your heads, keep your heads ! It's nothin'.

Michael [*beside himself with anxiety and dread — shaking Marion roughly by the shoulders*]. Conthrol yourself, girl, an' speak sensibly. Is it a goose or a duck or a hen, or what is it ?

Marion [*wildly*]. It's a goose — no, it's a hen, it must be a hen ! We thried to dhrive it out with flyin' cups and flyin' saucers, but it didn't notice them. Oh, some-one should go in, or it'll peck th' place to pieces !

Shanaar [*prayerfully*]. So long as it's not transmuted, so long as it's not been transmuted !

Michael [*shaking Marion again*]. Where's Lorna, where's Lorna ?

Marion [*responding to the shaking listlessly*]. Last I seen of her, she was barricadin' herself undher th' banisters !

Michael [*pleadingly — to Mahan*]. You've been free with whales an' dolphins an' octopususas, Sailor Mahan — you run in, like a good man, an' enthrone yourself on top of th' thing !

Mahan [*indignant*]. Is it me ? I'm not goin' to squandher meself conthrollin' live land-fowl !

Michael [*to Shanaar — half-commandingly*]. In case it's what we're afraid of, you pop in, Shanaar, an' liquidate whatever it is with your Latin.

Shanaar [*backing towards the wall*]. No good in th' house : it's effective only in th' open air.

Michael [*in a fury — to Marion — pushing her violently towards the gate*]. You go, you gapin', frightened fool, an' bring Father Domineer quick !

[*All this time, intermittent cackling has been heard, cackling with a note of satisfaction, or even victory in it, interspersed with the whirring sound of wings.*

[*As Marion rushes out through the gate, she runs into the arms of the Messenger, who carries a telegram in his hand. He clasps Marion tight in his arms, and kisses her. He wears a silvery-grey coat, buttoned over his breast, and*

trousers. On the right side of the coat is a flash of a pair
of scarlet wings. A bright-green beret is set jauntily on
his head and he is wearing green-coloured sandals.

[*Michael and Mahan have moved farther from the house, and*
Shanaar has edged to the gateway, where he stares at the
house, ready to run if anything happens. His hands are
piously folded in front of him, and his lips move as if he
prayed.

Messenger [*to Marion*]. Ah, lovely one of grace an' glad-
ness, whose kiss is like a honied flame, where are you
rushin' to in such a hurry?

Michael [*angrily — up to the Messenger*]. Let her go, you —
she's runnin' for th' priest!

Messenger. Th' priest — why?

[*The cackling breaks into intensity, the whirring of wings*
becomes louder, and a plate flies out through the window,
followed by a squeal from Lorna.

Messenger [*astonished, but not startled*]. What's goin' on in
th' house?

Michael. There's a wild-goose, or somethin', asthray in
th' house, an' it's sent th' althar bowl flyin'!

Marion. An' it's peckin' th' holy pictures hangin' on th'
walls.

Mahan. Some think it's a wild-duck.

Shanaar. It may be a hen, only a hen.

Messenger [*releasing Marion, and handing the telegram to*
Michael]. Here's a telegram for you. [*Michael takes it*
mechanically, and stuffs it in a pocket.] Is it losin' your

senses yous are to be afraid of a hen ? [*He goes towards the porch.*] I'll soon settle it !

Shanaar [*who is now outside, behind the wall*]. If you value your mortal life, lad, don't go in, for th' hen in there isn't a hen at all !

Messenger. If th' hen, that isn't a hen, in there, isn't a hen, then it must be a cock. I'll settle it !

> [*He rushes into the house.*

Michael [*in agony*]. If it's a cock, we're done !

Shanaar [*fervently*]. Oh, rowelum randee, horrida aidus, sed spero spiro specialii spam !

> [*The head of the Cock, with its huge, handsome crimson comb, is suddenly thrust through the window above the porch, and lets out a violent and triumphant crow. Shanaar disappears behind the wall, and Mahan and Michael fall flat in the garden, as if in a dead faint.*

Michael [*as he is falling*]. Holy saints preserve us — it's th' Cock !

Shanaar [*from behind the wall*]. Oh, dana eirebus, heniba et galli scatterum in multus parvum avic asthorum !

> [*The Cock's head is as suddenly withdrawn, and a louder commotion is heard to be going on in the house ; the Messenger shouting, a Woman's squeal. Then silence for a few moments as puffs of blue-black smoke jet out through the window. When the smoke has gone, the Messenger comes from the house into the garden. His cap is awry on his head, his face is a little flushed, and his mouth is smiling. He carries in his right hand what might have been a broomstick, but is now a silver staff, topped with a rosette of green and red ribbons. He is*

*followed out by the Cock whom he is leading by a green
ribbon, the other end circling the Cock's neck. The Cock
follows the Messenger meekly, stopping when he stops, and
moving when the Messenger moves.*

Shanaar [*peeping over the wall*]. Boys an' girls, take no
notice of it, or you're done ! Talk only of th' first
thing entherin' your minds.

Messenger [*looking with astonishment at the two men sitting up
now on the ground, as far as possible from the house, and moving
away when the Cock comes nearer*]. What's th' matther
with yous ? Why are yous dodgin' about on your
bums ? Get up, get up, an' be sensible.

[*Michael and Mahan scramble to their feet, hurry out
through the gate, and stand, warily, beside Shanaar.
Lorna's head appears at the window above the porch, and
it is at once evident that she is much younger than her
husband, very good-looking still, but the bright and
graceful contours of her face are somewhat troubled by a
vague aspect of worry and inward timidity. Her face
shows signs of excitement, and she speaks rather loudly
down to the Messenger.*

Lorna [*to the Messenger*]. Robin Adair, take that bird away
at once. Hand him over to th' Civic Guard, or some-
one fit to take charge of him.

Messenger [*up to Lorna*]. Looka, lovely lady, there's no
danger, an' there never was. He was lonely, an' was
only goin' about in quest o' company. Instead of
shyin' cups an' saucers at him, if only you'd given him
your lily-white hand, he'd have led you through a wistful
an' wondherful dance. But you frightened th' poor
thing !

Lorna. Frightened him, is it ? It was me was frightened
when I seen him tossin' down delf, clawin' holy
pictures, and peckin' to pieces th' brand new tall-hat
that Mr. Marthraun bought to wear, goin' with the
Mayor to greet His Brightness, th' President of Eire,
comin' to inaugerate th' new canteen for th' turf
workers.

Michael [*enraged*]. Is it me new hat he's desthroyed ?

Shanaar [*pulling Michael's arm in warning*]. Damnit, man,
take no notice !

Michael [*turning indignantly on Shanaar*]. How'd you like
your sumptuous, silken hat to be mangled into a
monstrosity !

Shanaar [*with concentrated venom*]. Hush, man, hush !

Marion [*who has been looking at the Cock with admiration*].
Sure, he's harmless when you know him.

Messenger [*stroking its back*]. 'Course he is ! Just a gay
bird, that's all. A bit unruly at times, but conthroll-
able be th' right persons. [*To the Cock*] Go on, comrade,
lift up th' head an' clap th' wings, black cock, an'
crow !

> [*The Cock lifts up his head, claps his wings, and lets out a
> mighty crow, which is immediately followed by a rumbling
> roll of thunder.*

Michael [*almost in a state of collapse*]. Aw, we're done for !

Shanaar [*violently*]. No notice, no notice !

Lorna [*from the window*]. God bless us, what's that ?
[*Down to the Messenger*] Robin, will you take that
damned animal away, before things happen that God
won't know about !

Messenger [*reassuringly — up to Lorna*]. Lovely lady, you can
let your little hands lie with idle quietness in your lap,
for there's no harm in him beyond gaiety an' fine
feelin'. [*To the Cock*] You know th' goose-step done be
the Irish Militia in th' city of Cork more'n a hundhred
years ago? Well, we'll go home doin' it, to show
there's nothing undher th' sun Ireland didn't know,
before th' world sensed it. Ready? One, two —
quick march!

> [*The Messenger and the Cock march off doing the goose-step.
> Marion follows them, imitating the step, as far as the end
> of the garden; then she stands looking after them, waving
> them farewell. Michael and Mahan come slowly and
> stealthily into the garden as the Cock goes out. They go
> to the chairs, on which they sit, exhausted, wiping their
> foreheads with their handkerchiefs. Shanaar comes
> towards them more slowly, keeping an eye in the direction
> taken by the Cock and the Messenger. When the place is
> clear, he anchors himself behind the table.*

Lorna [*down to Marion*]. Marion, dear, come on in, an'
help me to straighten things up a little.
> [*She goes away from the window.*

Marion [*going slowly towards the house, after having given a last
farewell — gleefully*]. Wasn't it a saucy bird! An' th'
stately way he done th' goose-step! [*She playfully shakes
Michael's shoulder*] Did you see it, sir? [*Michael takes no
notice.*] God forgive me, but it gave us all an hilarious
time — didn't it, sir?

Michael [*coldly*]. Your misthress called you.

Marion. I heard her, sir. What a clatther it all made!
An' yous all quakin', an' even Sailor Mahan there,
shakin' in his shoes, sure it was somethin' sinisther!

Mahan [*angrily*]. You go in to your misthress, girl !

Marion [*giggling*]. Th' bould sailor lad ! An' he gettin' rocked in th' cradle of th' deep ! Me faltherin' tongue can't impart th' fun I felt at seein' yous all thinkin' th' anchor was bein' weighed for th' next world !

Michael [*loudly*]. Go to your misthress when you're told.

Marion [*giggling more than ever*]. An' oul' dodderin' Shanaar, there, concoctin' his Latin, an' puttin' th' wall between himself an' th' blast ! Well, while yous sit all alone there in th' gloamin', yous won't be in heart for singin'. [*She chants*] " Only to see his face again, only to hear him crow ! "

[*She runs merrily in.*

Shanaar [*warily — in a warning whisper*]. Watch that one !

Michael. Th' ignorant, mockin', saucy face of her afther us bein' in danger of thransportation to where we couldn't know ourselves with agony an' consternation !

Shanaar [*fervently*]. Sweet airs of heaven be round us all ! Watch that one, Mr. Marthraun. Women is more flexible towards th' ungodly than us men, an' well th' old saints knew it. I'd recommend you to compel her, for a start, to lift her bodice higher up, an' pull her skirt lower down ; for th' circumnambulatory nature of a woman's form often has a detonatin' effect on a man's idle thoughts.

Michael [*pensively*]. How thrue, how thrue that is !

Shanaar. What we have to do now, is to keep thought from dwellin' on th' things seen an' heard this day ; for dwellin' on it may bring th' evil back again. So don't let any thought of it, *ab initio extensio*, remain in your minds, though, as a precaution, when I'm passin' th' barracks, I'll acquaint the Civic Guard. Now I must be off, for I've a long way to thravel. [*He goes as far as the gate, and returns.*] Mr. Marthraun, don't forget to have th' room, where th' commotion was manifested, *turbulenta concursio cockolorum*, purified an' surified be an understandin' clergyman. Goodbye. [*Again he goes as far as the gate, and returns.*] Be on your guard against any unfamiliar motion or peculiar conspicuosity or quasimodical addendum, perceivable in any familiar thing or creature common to your general recognisances. A cat barkin' at a dog, or a dog miaouin' be a fire would atthract your attention, give you a shock, but don't, for th' love of God, notice it! It's this scourge of materialism sweepin' th' world, that's incantatin' these evils to our senses and our doorsteps.

Mahan [*pensively*]. That's th' way th' compass is pointin', Shanaar — everyone only thinkin', thinkin' of himself.

Shanaar. An' women's wily exhilarations are abettin' it, so that a man's measure of virtue is now made with money, used to buy ornaments, bestowed on girls to give a gaudy outside to the ugliness of hell.

Michael [*fervently*]. Oh, how thrue, how thrue that is!

Shanaar. An' th' coruscatin' conduct in th' dance-halls is completin' th' ruin.

Mahan [*solemnly*]. Wise words from a wiser man! Afther a night in one of them, there isn't an ounce of energy left in a worker!

Shanaar [*whispering*]. A last warnin'— Don't forget that six thousand six hundhred an' sixty-six evil spirits can find ready lodgin's undher th' skin of a single man!

C

Michael [*horrified*]. What an appallin' thought !

Shanaar. So be on your guard. Well, goodbye.

Michael [*offering him a note*]. Here's a pound to help you on your way.

Shanaar [*setting the note aside*]. No, thanks. If I took it, I couldn't fuse th' inner with th' outher vision ; I'd lose th' power of spiritual scansion. If you've a shillin' for a meal in th' town till I get to the counthry, where I'm always welcome, I'll take it, an' thank you.

[*Michael gives him a shilling.*

Shanaar. Thank you kindly. [*He goes out through the gate, and along the pathway outside. Just as he is about to disappear, he faces towards the two men, and stretches out a hand in a gesture of blessing. Fervently*] Ab tormentum sed absolvo, non revolvo, cockalorum credulum hibernica !

Michael [*with emotion*]. You too, Shanaar, oul' son ; you too !

[*Shanaar goes off.*

Mahan [*after a pause — viciously*]. That Latin-lustrous oul' cod of a prayer-blower is a positive danger goin' about th' counthry !

Michael [*startled and offended*]. Eh ? I wouldn't go callin' him a cod, Sailor Mahan. A little asthray in a way, now an' again, but no cod. You should be th' last to call th' man a cod, for if it wasn't for his holy Latin aspirations, you mightn't be here now.

Mahan [*with exasperation*]. Aw, th' oul' fool, pipin' a gale into every breeze that blows ! I don't believe there was ever anything engenderogically evil in that cock as a cock, or denounceable either ! Lardin' a man's mind with his killakee Latin ! An' looka th' way he slights th' women. I seen him lookin' at Lorna an' Marion as if they'd horns on their heads !

Michael [*doubtfully*]. Maybe he's too down on th' women, though you have to allow women is temptin'.

Mahan. They wouldn't tempt man if they didn't damn well know he wanted to be tempted !

Michael. Yes, yes ; but we must suffer th' temptation accordin' to the cognisances of th' canon law. But let's have a dhrink, for I'm near dead with th' drouth, an' we can sensify our discussion about th' increased price you're demandin' for carryin' th' turf ; though, honest to God, Sailor Mahan, I can't add a ha'penny more to what I'm givin'.

Mahan. A dhrink would be welcome, an' we can talk over th' matter, though, honest to God, Michael Marthraun, blast th' penny less I'll take than what I'm askin'.

Michael [*going to the porch, and shouting into the house*]. Marion, bring th' bottle of ten years' maturin', an' two glasses ! [*He returns.*] It's th' principle I'm thinkin' of.

Mahan. That's what's throublin' me, too. [*Marion comes in with the bottle of whiskey and the two glasses. She places them on the table, getting between the two men to do so. Reading the label*] Flanagan's First ! Nyav na Nyale — th' heaven of th' clouds ! An' brought be a lass who's a Flanagan's first too !

Marion [*in jovial mood*]. G'long with you — you an' your blarney !

Michael [*enthusiastically*]. Had you lived long ago, Emer would have been jealous of you !

> [*He playfully pinches her bottom.*

Marion [*squealing*]. Ouch ! [*She breaks away, and makes for the porch.*] A pair o' naughty men !

> [*She goes into the house.*

Michael [*calling after her*]. I forgot th' soda, Marion ; bring th' siphon, lass.

Mahan [*complacently*]. I could hold that one in me arms for a long time, Mick.

Michael. Th' man would want to be dead who couldn't.

Mahan [*enthusiastically*]. I'd welcome her, even if I seen her through th' vision of oul' Shanaar — with horns growin' out of her head !

> [*Marion returns with the siphon which she places on the table. The Two Men, looking in front of them, have silly, sly grins on their faces.*

> [*The ornament, which Marion wears round her head, has separated into two parts, each of which has risen over her head, forming two branching horns, apparently sprouting from her forehead. The Two Men, shyly gazing in front, or at the table, do not see the change. Marion's face has changed too, and now seems to wear a mocking, cynical look, fitting the aspect of her face to the horns.*

Marion [*joking*]. Two wild men — it's afraid I am to come near yous.

> [*Michael puts his right arm round her waist, and Mahan his left one.*

Mahan [*slyly*]. What about a kiss on your rosy mouth, darlin', to give a honied tang to th' whiskey ?

Michael. An' one for me, too ?

Marion [*with pretended demureness*]. A thrue gentleman'll rise up an' never expect a thrue lady to bend down for a kiss. [*With vigour*] Up an' take it, before yous grow cold !

> [*They rise from their chairs, foolish grins on their faces, settle themselves for a kiss, and then perceive the change that has taken place. They flop back on to the chairs, fright and dismay sweeping over their faces.*

Mahan }
Michael } [*together*].   Good God !

> [*They slump in the chairs, overcome, their hands folded in front of their chests, palm to palm, as if in prayer. Marion looks at them in some astonishment.*

Marion. What ails yous ? Was th' excitement too much for yous, or what ?

Michael [*plaintively*]. Saints in heaven help us now !

Marion. What's come over yous ? Th' way yous slumped so sudden down, you'd think I'd horns on me, or somethin' !

Michael [*hoarsely*]. G'way, g'way ! Shanaar, Shanaar, where are you now !

Marion [*going over to Mahan, and putting an arm round his neck*]. What about you, gay one ?

Mahan [*gurgling with fright*]. You're sthranglin' me ! G'way, g'way, girl !

Marion. Looka, a kiss would do yous good. Yous think too much of th' world !

Mahan [*chokingly*]. St. Christopher, mainstay of mariners, be with me now !

> [*Lorna thrusts her head out from the window over the porch.*

Lorna [*down to Marion*]. Let them two oul' life-frighteners fend for themselves, an' come in. From th' back window, I can see th' crowd gathered to give Julia a send-off to Lourdes, so come in to tidy if you want to join them with me.

Marion [*half to herself — as she runs into the house*]. God forgive me — I near forgot ! Here we are followin' laughter, instead of seekin' succour from prayer !

> [*She runs in, and Lorna takes her head back into the room again.*

Michael [*frightened and very angry*]. Now, maybe, you'll quit your jeerin' at oul' Shanaar ! Now, maybe, you'll let your mind concentrate on higher things ! Now, maybe, you won't be runnin' loose afther girls !

Mahan [*indignantly*]. Damnit, man, you were as eager for a cuddle as I was !

Michael [*lifting his eyes skywards*]. Oh, d'ye hear that ! I was only toleratin' your queer declivity, like a fool. An' afther all th' warnin's given be wise oul' Shanaar ! Looka, Sailor Mahan, you'll have to be more on your guard !

Mahan [*trying to defend himself*]. How could any man suspect such a thing ? We'll have to think this thing out.

Michael [*with exasperation*]. Think it out ! Oh, man,

Sailor Mahan, have you nothin' more sensible to say than that we'll have to think it out ?

Mahan. Let's have a dhrink, for God's sake, to steady us down !

Michael [*hurriedly putting bottle and glasses under the table*]. What're you thinkin' of, Sailor Mahan ? We can't dispense ourselves through a scene of jollification an' poor Julia passin' on her way to Lourdes !

> [*Along the path, on a stretcher, carried by the two Rough Fellows, comes Julia, followed by her father. The stretcher is borne to the gate, and there laid down, so that the head of it is flush with the gate-posts, and the rest of it within the garden. The framework of the gate makes a frame for Julia, who is half sitting up, her head supported by a high pillow. Her face is a sad yellowish mask, pierced by wide eyes, surrounded by dark circles. Her father is a sturdy fellow of fifty, a scraggly greyish beard struggling from his chin. He is roughly dressed as a poorer peasant might be, and his clothes are patched in places. He wears a brown muffler, and a faded black trilby-hat is on his head. All the time, he looks straight in front with a passive and stony stare.*

> [*Before the stretcher walks the Mayor, rather stout, clean-shaven, wearing a red robe over rough clothing ; he has a very wide three-cornered hat, laced with gold, on his head. Behind him walks the Mace-bearer, a big silver and black mace on his shoulder. He is tall, and wears a bright blue robe, trimmed with silver, on his head is a huge cocked hat, laced, too, with silver. These two do not enter the garden, but walk on, and stand waiting near the house, beside the flag-pole, but without the wall.*

> [*Lorna, followed by Marion, comes out of the house. Instead of the bright headgear worn before, they have black*

kerchiefs, worn peasant-wise on their heads — that is, they have been folded triangularly, draped over their heads, with the ends tied beneath their chins.

[*Lorna runs over to the stretcher, kneels down beside it, and kisses Julia.*]

Lorna [*affectionately*]. My sister, my little Julia, oh, how sorry I am that you have to go on this long, sad journey !

Julia [*her voice is low, but there is a hectic note of hope in it*]. A long journey, Lorna darlin', but not a sad one ; oh, no, not a sad one. Hope, Lorna, will have me be the hand all the long way. I go to kneel at the feet of the ever Blessed Virgin.

Lorna. Oh, she will comfort you, me darlin'.

Julia. Yes, she will comfort me, Lorna [*after a pause*] ; an' cure me too. Lorna, say she will cure me too.

Lorna [*stifling a sob*]. An' cure you, too.

Julia [*to Michael*]. Give me your good wishes, Mr. Marthraun.

Michael [*with genuine emotion*]. Julia, me best wishes go with you, an' me best prayers'll follow all th' long way !

Julia [*to Mahan*]. An' you, Sailor Mahan — have you no good wish for the poor voyager ?

Mahan [*fervently*]. Young lass, may you go through healin' wathers, an' come back a clipper, with ne'er a spar, a sail, or a rope asthray !

[*Father Domineer comes quickly in on the path outside. He is a tall, rather heavily built man of forty. He has a breezy manner now, heading the forlorn hope. He is trying to smile now, but crack his mouth as he will, the tight, surly lines of his face refuse to furnish one. He is dressed in the usual clerical, outdoor garb, and his hard head is covered with a soft, rather widely brimmed black hat.*

Father Domineer [*as happily as he can*]. Now, now, no halts on th' road, little daughter ! The train won't wait, an' we must have a few minutes to spare to make you comfortable. Bring her along, Brancardiers ! Forward, in th' name o' God and of Mary, ever Virgin, ever blessed, always bending to help poor, banished children of Eve !

[*The two Rough Men take up the stretcher, and carry it along the pathway outside, the Mayor, followed by his Mace-bearer, leading it on. Father Domineer follows immediately behind ; then come Lorna and Marion, followed by Michael and Mahan.*

[*As the stretcher moves along the pathway outside, a band in the distance is heard playing " Star of the Sea ", to which is added the voice of a crowd singing the words :*

Hail, Queen of Heaven, the ocean Star !
Guide of the wand'rer here below !
Thrown on life's surge, we claim thy care —
Save us from peril and from woe.

Mother of Christ, Star of the Sea,
Pray for the wanderer, pray for me.

Father Domineer [*enthusiastically*]. Julia will bring us back a miracle, a glorious miracle ! To Lourdes !

END OF SCENE I

Scene II

The Scene is the same as before, though the sunshine isn't quite so bright and determined. The Irish tricolour flies breezily from its flag-pole ; the table and chairs stand where they were, and the bottle and glasses are still under it.

No-one is in the garden, all, apparently, having gone to see Julia away on her long, long journey. Away in the distance the band is playing " Star of the Sea ", and the tune can be softly heard from the garden.

After a few moments, Lorna and Marion come along the path outside, enter by the gate, and cross over into the house.

Marion [*anxiously*]. What d'ye think of th' chance of a cure ?

Lorna. I'm afraid th' chance is a poor one ; but we won't talk about it.

Marion [*piously*]. Well, it was a grand send-off, an' God is good.

Lorna [*coldly*]. An' th' devil's not a bad fella either.

> [*They both go into the house, and, a few moments later, Michael and Mahan stroll along the path, come into the garden, and go to where the table and chairs are.*

Mahan. Well, th' anchor's weighed.

Michael. It was an edifyin' spectacle, Sailor Mahan, thrustin' us outa this world for th' time bein'. Julia's asked for a sign, Sailor Mahan, an', believe me, she'll get it.

Mahan. She will, she will, though I wouldn't like to bet on it.

Michael. She'll get what she's afther — a complete cure. Me own generous gift of fifty pounds for th' oul' bog'll be rewarded ; an' th' spate o' prayin' goin' on, from th' Mayor to the Bellman, is bound to get th' higher saints goin', persuadin' them to furnish a suitable answer to all we're askin'.

Mahan [*impatiently*]. Arra, man alive, d'ye think th' skipper aloft an' his glitterin' crew is goin' to bother their heads about a call from a tiny town an' disthrict thryin' hard to thrive on turf ?

Michael [*indignantly*]. Looka, if you were only versed in th' endurin' promulgacity of th' gospels, you'd know th' man above's concerned as much about Nyadnanave as he is about a place where a swarm of cardinals saunther secure, decoratin' th' air with all their purple an' gold !

Mahan [*as indignantly*]. Are you goin' to tell me that th' skipper aloft an' his hierarchilogical crew are concerned about th' Mayor, the Messenger, Marion, me, an' you as much as they are about them who've been promoted to th' quarter-deck o' th' world's fame ? Are you goin' to pit our palthry penances an' haltin' hummin' o' hymns against th' piercin' pipin' of th' rosary be Bing Bang Crosby an' other great film stars, who side-stepped from published greatness for a holy minute or two to send a blessed blast over th' wireless, callin' all Catholics to perpetuatin' prayer !

Michael [*sitting down on a chair*]. Sailor Mahan, I ask you to thry to get your thoughts ship-shaped in your mind.

[*While they have been talking, the Messenger has come running along the path outside, and is now leaning on the gate, listening to the two men, unnoticed by them.*

Mahan [*plumping down on the other chair — indignantly*]. D'ye remember who you're talkin' to, man ? Ship-shape in me mind ! Isn't a man bound to have his mind fitted together in a ship-shape way, who, forced out of his thrue course be a nautical cathastrope, to wit, videliket, an act o' God, ploughed a way through th' Sargasso Sea, reachin' open wathers, long afther hope had troubled him no longer ?

Michael [*wearily*]. Aw, Sailor Mahan, what's them things got to do with th' things tantamount to heaven ?

Messenger [*over to them*]. Mick's right — them things can't be tantamount to anything bar themselves.

Mahan [*turning fiercely on the Messenger*]. What do you want ? What're you doin' here ? Your coalition of ignorant knowledge can't comprehend th' things we talk about !

Messenger [*with some excitement*]. Listen, boys — I've a question to ask yous.

Michael [*with a gesture signifying this isn't the time to ask it*]. Ask it some time more convenient. An' don't refer to us as ' boys ' — we're gentlemen to you !

Mahan [*to Michael*]. Looka, Mick, if you only listened to Bing Crosby, th' mighty film star, croonin' his Irish lullaby, [*he chants*] " Tooral ooral ooral, tooral ooral ay ", you'd have th' visuality to see th' amazin' response he'd have from millions of admirers, if he crooned a hymn !

Messenger. I was never sthruck be Bing Crosby's croonin'.

Michael [*wrathfully — to Messenger*]. You were never sthruck ! An' who th' hell are you to be consulted ? Please don't stand there interferin' with the earnest colloquy of betther men. [*To Mahan*] Looka, Sailor Mahan, any priest'll tell you that in th' eyes of heaven all men are equal an' must be held in respect an' reverence.

Mahan [*mockingly*]. Ay, they'll say that to me an' you, but will they say it to Bing Crosby, or any other famous film star ?

Messenger. Will they hell ! Honour be th' clergy's regulated by how much a man can give !

Michael [*furiously — to the Messenger*]. Get to hell outa here ! With that kinda talk, we won't be able soon to sit steady on our chairs. Oh !

[*The chair he is sitting on collapses, and he comes down to the ground on his arse.*

Mahan [*astonished*]. Holy saints, what's happened ?

Michael [*in a fierce whisper — to Mahan*]. Take no notice of it, fool. Go on talkin' !

Mahan [*a little confused*]. I'll say you're right, Mick ; th' way things are goin' we won't be able much longer to sit serene on our chairs. Oh !

[*The chair collapses under Mahan, and he, too, comes down to the ground.*

Michael [*in a fierce whisper*]. Don't notice it ; go on's if nothin' happened !

Messenger [*amused*]. Well, yous have settled down now, anyhow ! Will I get yous chairs sturdy enough to uphold th' wisdom of your talkin ?

Michael [*angrily — to Messenger*]. There's nothin' wrong with th' chairs we have! You get outa here! Nothin's wrong with th' chairs at all. Get outa here — I don't trust you either!

Messenger. I've somethin' important to ask yous.

Michael. Well, ask it at some more convenient time. [*To Mahan*] It's a blessin' that so many lively-livin' oul' holy spots are still in th' land to help us an' keep us wary.

Messenger [*scornfully*]. An' where are th' lively holy spots still to be found? Sure, man, they're all gone west long ago, an' the whole face o' th' land is pock-marked with their ruins!

Michael [*shouting at the Messenger*]. Where are th' lost an' ruined holy places? We've always cared for, an' honoured, our holy spots! Mention one of them, either lost or ruined!

Messenger [*shouting back*]. There are thousands of them, man; places founded be Finian, Finbarr, an' th' rest; places that are now only an oul' ruined wall, blighted be nettle an' dock, their only glory, th' crimson berries of th' bright arbutus! Where's th' Seven Churches of Glendalough? Where's Durrow of Offally, founded be Columkille himself? Known now only be the name of the Book of Durrow!

Michael [*ferociously*]. Book o' Durrow! It's books that have us half th' woeful way we are, fillin' broody minds with loose scholasticality, infringin' th' holy beliefs an' thried impositions that our fathers' fathers' fathers gave our fathers' fathers, who gave our fathers what our fathers gave to us!

Messenger. Faith, your fathers' faith is fear, an' now fear is your only fun.

Mahan [*impatiently*]. Let him go, Mick, an' let's have that dhrink you mentioned a year ago.

   [*Marion's head appears at the window, looking down at the Messenger. The decorations on her head have now declined to their first place.*

Marion [*down to the Messenger*]. Hallo, Robin Adair! [*He looks up.*] Where are th' two oul' woeful wondhers? [*He points to where they are.*] Oh, they've brought the unsteady chairs out, and now they've broken them up! [*To Michael — angrily*] You knew well th' chairs in the hall were there only to present an appearance.

Messenger [*up to her*]. Oh, Marion, Marion, sweet Marion, come down till I give you a kiss havin' in it all the life an' longin' of th' greater lovers of th' past!

Marion [*leaving the window*]. Now, now, naughty boy!

Michael [*sourly*]. You'd do well to remember, lad, the month in jail you got for kissin' Marion, an' the forty-shillin' fine on Marion, for kissing you in a public place at th' cross-roads.

   [*Marion comes from the house, goes toward the Messenger, who seizes her in his arms, and kisses her.*

Messenger. I'd do a year an' a day in a cold cell of pressed-in loneliness, an' come out singin' a song, for a kiss from a lass like Marion!

Marion. Don't think too much of me, Robin Adair, for I've some of th' devil in me, an' th' two fostherers of fear, there, think I wear horns on holy days.

Michael [*impressively*]. See — she's warnin' you, herself, young man !

Marion [*to the Messenger*]. An' what has you here arguin' with them two oul' fools ?

Messenger. I came to ask a question of them, but they were buried in their prayers. Did you see him ? Did he come this way ?

Michael [*suddenly alarmed*]. Come where ?

Mahan [*alarmed*]. See who ?

Messenger. Th' Cock.

Mahan ⎫
Michael ⎭ [*together*]. Th' Cock !

> [*They carefully creep away from the broken chairs, and stand up when they are some distance from them.*

Messenger. Ay. I thought he'd make for here first.

Michael [*echoing the Messenger*]. Make for here first !

> [*In the distance, the loud, exultant crow of the Cock is heard.*

Messenger [*excitedly*]. There he is ! Away in the direction east of th' bog ! I'll go, get him, an' fetch him home.

Marion [*kissing the Messenger*]. Bring him here first, Robin, an' I'll have a wreath of roses ready to hang round his neck.

Messenger [*rushing away*]. I will, I will, fair one !

> [*He goes off. She takes the broken chairs into the house.*

Marion [*carrying in the chairs*]. Next time, you boyos, take out two steady ones.

Michael [*horrified*]. Did you hear what she said, Sailor Mahan? Hang a wreath of roses round his neck! Well, I'll have th' gun ready! Ay, now!

  [*He goes over to the porch, but Mahan lays a restraining hand on his arm.*

Mahan. What good would th' gun be? Have you forgot what Shanaar told us? Your bullet would go clean through him, an' leave him untouched. Now that we're in peace here, let's have th' dhrink we were to have, an' which we both need.

Michael [*halting*]. You're right, Sailor Mahan. If he comes here, what we have to do is to take no notice. Look through him, past him, over him, but never at him. [*He prepares the bottle of whiskey and the glasses.*] There's sinisther enchantments all around us. God between us an' all harm! We'll have to be for ever on our guard.

Mahan [*impatiently*]. Yis, yis; fill out th' dhrink for God's sake!

Michael. May it give us courage. [*He tilts the bottle over the glass, but none of it spills out.*] Good God, th' bottle's bewitched too!

Mahan. Bottle bewitched? How could a bottle be bewitched? Steady your nerves, man. Thry givin' it a shake.

Michael [*who has left the bottle back on the table — retreating away from it*]. Thry givin' it a shake yourself, since you're so darin'.

  [*Mahan goes over to the table with a forced swagger, and reaches out a cautious hand for the bottle. As he touches it, its colour changes to a glowing red.*

D

Mahan [*fervent and frightened*]. St. Christopher, pathron of all mariners, defend us — th' bottle's changed its colour !

Michael. There's evil things cantherin' an' crawlin' about this place ! You saw th' seal on th' bottle showin' it was untouched since it left th' store. Flanagan's finest, Jamieson's best, ten years maturin' — an' look at it now.

Mahan. How are we goin' to prevent ourselves from bein' the victims of sorcery an' ruin ? You'd think good whiskey would be exempt from injury even be th' lowest of th' low.

Michael. It's th' women who're always intherceptin' our good intentions. Evil things is threatenin' us everywhere. Th' one safe method of turnin' our back to a power like this is to go forward an' meet it half-way. [*He comes close to Mahan, and whispers hoarsely*] Selah !

Mahan [*mystified and frightened at what he thinks may be something sinister*]. Selah ?

Michael [*emphatically*]. Selah !

Mahan [*agonisingly*]. Good God !

Michael. Now, maybe, you'll believe what th' Missioner said last night.

Mahan [*a little dubiously*]. He might have been exaggeratin' a bit, Mick.

Michael. Look at th' bottle, man ! Demons can hide in th' froth of th' beer a man's dhrinkin'. An' all th' time, my turf-workers an' your lorry drivers are screwin' all they can out of us so that they'll have more to spend on pictures an' in th' dance halls, leavin' us to face th' foe alone.

Mahan [*abjectly*]. What's a poor, good-livin', virtuous man to do then?

Michael. He must always be thinkin' of th' four last things — hell, heaven, death, an' th' judgement.

Mahan [*pitifully*]. But that would sthrain a man's nerves, an' make life hardly worth livin'.

Michael. It's plain, Sailor Mahan, you're still hankerin' afther th' things o' th' world, an' the soft, stimulatin' touch of th' flesh. You're puttin' th' two of us in peril, Sailor Mahan.

Mahan [*protesting*]. You're exaggeratin' now.

Michael. I am not. I seen your eyes followin' that Loreleen when she's about, hurtin' th' tendher muscles of your eye squintin' down at her legs. You'll have to curb your conthradictions, for you're puttin' us both in dire peril, Sailor Mahan. Looka what I've lost already! Me fine silk hat torn to shreds, so that Lorna's had to telephone th' Firm for another, that I may suitably show meself when I meet his Brightness, the President; an' looka th' whiskey there — forced into a mis-undherstandin' of itself be some minor demon devisin' a spell on it! Guess how much good money I sur-rendhered to get that bottle, Sailor Mahan?

Mahan. I've no idea of what whiskey is a gallon now.

Michael [*impatiently*]. What whiskey is a gallon now? Is there some kinda spell on you, too, Sailor Mahan? You can't think of whiskey in gallons now; you have to think of it in terms of sips ; an' sips spaced out from each other like th' holy days of obligation.

Mahan. An' how are we goin' to get rid of it ? We're in some danger while it's standin' there.

Michael. How th' hell do I know how we'll get rid of it? We'll have to get Shanaar to deal with it, an', mind you, don't go too near it.

[*The Porter appears on the sidewalk outside the wall. He is a middle-aged man with an obstinate face, the chin hidden by a grizzled beard. He is wearing a pair of old brown trousers, an older grey coat, and an old blue shirt. On his head is a big cap, with a long, wide peak jutting out in front of it. The crown of the cap is a high one, and around the crown is a wide band of dazzling scarlet. He is carrying a parcel wrapped in brown paper, either side of which is a little torn. He looks north, south, west, and then, turning east, he sees the two men in the garden.*]

Porter [*to the two men*]. Isn't it handy now that I've clapped eyes on two human bein's in this god-forsaken hole ! I've been trudghin' about for hours thryin' to find th' one that'll claim what's in this parcel I'm bearin', an', maybe, th' two of yous, or maybe, one of yous, can tell me where I'll find him. I'm on th' thrack of an oul' fella callin' himself a Councillor an' a Jay Pee.

Michael. What's his name ?

Porter. That's more than I can say, for th' chit of th' girl in th' shop, who took th' ordher, forgot to write down th' name, an' then forgot th' name itself when she started to write it down. All I know is that in this disthrict I'm seekin' a Mr. Councillor So-an'-so ; one havin' Councillor at his head an' Jay Pee at his tail.

Michael [*with importance*]. I'm a Councillor and a Jay Pee.

Porter [*with some scorn*]. D'ye tell me that now ? [*He bends over the wall to come closer to Michael*]. Listen, me good man, me journey's been too long an' too dangerous for me to glorify any cod-actin' ! It would be a quare place if you were a councillor. You'll have to grow a few more grey hairs before you can take a rise outa me !

Michael [*indignantly*]. Tell us what you've got there, fella', an', if it's not for us, be off about your business !

Porter [*angrily*]. Fella yourself ! An' mend your manners, please ! It's hardly th' like of you would be standin' in need of a silky, shinin' tall-hat.

Michael. If it's a tall-hat, it's for me ! I'm Mr. Councillor Marthraun, Jay Pee — ordhered to be sent express by th' firm of Buckley's.

Porter [*with a quick conciliatory change*]. That's th' firm. I guessed you was th' man at once, at once. That man's a leadher in th' locality, I said, as soon as I clapped me eye on you. A fine, clever, upstandin' individual, I says to meself.

Michael [*shortly*]. Hand over th' hat, and you can go.

Porter. Hould on a minute, sir ; wait till I tell you : I'm sorry, but th' hat's been slightly damaged in thransit.

           [*He begins to take the hat from the paper.*

Michael. Damaged ? How th' hell did you damage it ?

Porter. Me, is it ? No, not me, sir. [*He stretches over the wall towards them.*] When I was bringin' it here, some-one shot a bullet through it, east be west !

Michael. Nonsense, man, who'd be shootin' bullets round here ?

Porter. Who indeed ? That's th' mystery. Bullet it was. People told me the Civic Guards were out thryin' to shoot down an evil spirit flyin' th' air in th' shape of a bird.

Michael [alarmed]. Th' Cock !

Porter [placing the tall-hat on the wall carefully]. An' seein' how things are, an' th' fright I got, it's welcome a dhrink would be from th' handsome bottle I see paradin' on th' table.

Michael [in a loud whisper]. To touch it is to go in danger of your life — th' bottle's bewitched !

Porter. Th' bottle bewitched ? What sort of a place have me poor, wandherin' feet sthrayed into at all ? Before I ventured to come here at all, I should have stayed at home. I'm already as uneasy as th' place itself ! *[A shot is heard, and the tall-hat is knocked from the wall on to the road.]* Saints in glory, there's another one !

Mahan [excitedly]. It's your hat, man, th' red band on your hat !

Porter [to Michael — speaking rapidly, picking the tall-hat from the road and offering it to Michael.] Here, take your hat, sir, an' keep it safe, an' I'll be goin'.

Michael [frightened and angry]. Take it back ; it's damaged ; take it back, fella !

Porter [loudly and with anger]. Fella yourself ! Is it takin' th' risk I'd be of a bullet rushin' through me instead of th' oul' hat ? *[He flings it towards the two men.]* Here,

take your oul' hat an' th' risk along with it ! Do what
you want with it ; do what you like with it ; do what
you can with it — I'm off !

[*He runs off in the direction he came from, while the two
men gaze doubtfully at the hat lying in the garden.*

Michael [*tremulously*]. The cowards that are in this
counthry — leavin' a poor man alone in his dilemma !
I'd be afraid to wear it now.

Mahan. Aw, give yourself a shake, Mick. You're not
afraid of a poor tall-hat. An' throw away ten good
pounds.

[*He goes toward where the hat is, but Michael holds him by
the arm.*

Michael [*with warning and appeal*]. No, don't touch it till
we see further.

[*The Sergeant appears on the pathway outside. He has a
rifle in his hands; he leans against the wall looking
towards the two. He is obviously anxious, and in a
state of fear.*

Sergeant. Yous didn't see it ? It didn't come here, did
it ?

Michael [*breathless with the tension of fear*]. No, no ; not
yet. [*With doleful appeal*] Oh, don't be prowlin' round
here — you'll only be attractin' it to th' place !

Sergeant [*ignoring appeal*]. Three times I shot at it ; three
times th' bullets went right through it ; and twice th'
thing flew away crowing.

Michael [*excitedly*]. Did you get it th' third time, did you
get it then ?

Sergeant. Wait till I tell yous : sthrange things an' unruly
are happenin' in this holy land of ours this day ! Will
I ever forget what happened th' third time I hot it !
Never, never. Isn't it a wondher an' a mercy of God
that I'm left alive afther th' reverberatin' fright I got !

Michael [*eagerly*]. Well, what happened when you hot it
then ?

Mahan [*eagerly*]. When you hot it for th' third time ?

Sergeant. Yous could never guess ?

Michael [*impatiently*]. Oh, we know we'd never guess ;
no one can go guessin' about demonological disturb-
ances.

Mahan. Tell us, will you, without any more of your
sthructural suggestions !

Sergeant. As sure as I'm standin' here ; as sure as sure as
this gun is in me left hand ; [*He is holding it in his right
one*] as sure as we're all poor, identified sinners ; when
I hot him for th' third time, I seen him changin' into
a——

Michael
Mahan } [*together*]. What ?

Sergeant [*whisperingly*]. What d'ye think ?

Mahan [*explosively*]. Oh, we're not thinkin' ; we can't
think ; we're beyond thinkin' ! We're waitin' for you
to tell us !

Sergeant. Th' soul well-nigh left me body when I seen
th' unholy novelty happenin' : th' thing that couldn't
be, yet th' thing that was. If I never prayed before, I
prayed then — for hope ; for holy considheration in

th' quandary ; for power to be usual an' spry again
when th' thing was gone.

Michael. What thing, what thing, man ?

Mahan [*despairingly*]. Thry to tell us, Sergeant, what you
said you said you seen.

Sergeant. I'm comin' to it ; since what I seen was seen
by no man never before, it's not easy for a man to
describe with evidential accuracy th' consequential
thoughts fluttherin' through me amazed mind at what
was, an' what couldn't be, demonstrated there, or
there, or anywhere else, where mortals congregate in
ones or twos or crowds astoundin'.

Michael [*imploringly*]. Looka, Sergeant, we're languishin'
for th' information that may keep us from spendin'
th' rest of our lives in constant consternation.

Sergeant. As I was tellin' you, there was th' crimson crest
of th' Cock, enhancin' th' head lifted up to give a
crow, an' when I riz th' gun to me shoulder, an' let
bang, th' whole place went dead dark ; a flash of red
lightning near blinded me ; an' when it got light
again, a second afther, there was the demonised Cock
changin' himself into a silken glossified tall-hat !

Michael [*horrified*]. A silken tall-hat !

Mahan. A glossified tall-hat !

Michael [*to Mahan — viciously*]. Now you'll quit undher-
estimatin' what th' holy Missioner said last night
about th' desperate an' derangin' thrickeries of evil
things loose an' loungin' among us ! Now can you see
the significality of things ?

Mahan [*going away as far as he can from the tall-hat lying in the garden*]. Steer clear of it ; get as far away from it as we can !   Keep well abaft of it !

Sergeant [*puzzled*]. Keep clear from what ?

Mahan [*pointing to the hat*]. Th' hat, man, th' hat !

Sergeant [*seeing the hat beside him, and jumping away from it*]. I was near touchin' th' brim of it !   Jasus ! yous should have warned me !

Michael [*close to the Sergeant — in a whisper*]. Does it look anything like th' thing you shot ?

Sergeant [*laying a shaking hand on Michael's arm*]. It's th' dead spit of what I seen him changin' into durin' th' flash of lightning !   I just riz th' gun to me shouldher — like this [*he raises the gun to his shoulder*] to let bang.

[*The garden is suddenly enveloped in darkness for a few moments.   A fierce flash of lightning shoots through the darkness ; the hat has disappeared, and where it stood now stands the Cock.   While the lightning flashes, the Cock crows lustily.   Then the light as suddenly comes back to the garden, and shows that the Cock and the hat have gone.   Michael and Mahan are seen to be lying on the ground, and the Sergeant is on his knees, as if in prayer.*

Sergeant. Holy St. Custodius, pathron of th' police, protect me !

Michael [*in a whisper*]. Are you there, Sailor Mahan ?

Mahan [*in a whisper*]. Are you there, Michael Marthraun ?

Michael. I'm done for.

Mahan. We're both done for.

Sergeant. We're all done for.

Mahan. Th' smell of th' sulphur an' brimstone's burnin' me.

Michael. Now you'll give up mockin' Shanaar, if it's not too late. You seen how Marion's head was ornamented, an' it'll not be long till Lorna has them too.

Sergeant [*now sitting down, so that he is to the left of Michael, while Mahan sits to the right of him, so frightened that he must blame someone*]. We'll have to curtail th' gallivantin' of th' women afther th' men. Th' house is their province, as th' clergy's tired tellin' them. They'll have to realise that th' home's their only proper place.

Michael. An' demolish th' minds that babble about books.

Sergeant [*raising his voice*]. Th' biggest curse of all ! Books no decent mortal should touch, should never even see th' cover of one !

Michael [*warningly*]. Hush ! Don't speak so loud, or th' lesser boyo'll hear you !

Sergeant [*startled*]. Lesser boyo ? What lesser boyo ?

Mahan [*whispering and pointing*]. Th' boyo in th' bottle there.

Sergeant [*noticing it for the first time*]. Why, what's in it ?

Michael. Th' best of whiskey was in it till some evil spirit put a spell on it, desthroyin' its legitimate use.

Sergeant [*unbelievingly*]. I don't believe it. Nothin' could translate good dhrink into anything but what it was made to be. We could do with a dhrink now.
                    [*He advances cautiously towards the table.*

Michael [*excitedly*]. Don't meddle with it, man ; don't stimulate him !

> [*The Sergeant tiptoes over to the table, stretches his hand out, and touches the bottle. He immediately lets out a yelp, and jumps back.*

Sergeant. Oh ! Be God, it's red-hot !

Mahan [*angrily*]. You were told not to touch it ! You're addin' to our dangers.

Michael [*shouting*]. Good God, man, couldn't you do what you're told ! Now you've added anger to its impositional qualities !

Sergeant [*nursing his hand*]. Aren't we in a nice quandary when an evil thing can insconce itself in a bottle !

Michael. Th' whole place's seethin' with them. You, Sergeant, watch th' road north ; you, Sailor Mahan, watch it south ; an' I'll keep an eye on th' house. [*Mahan goes to one end of the wall, the Sergeant to the other, and both stretch over it to look different ways along the road. During the next discussion, whenever they leave where they are, they move cautiously, crouching a little, as if they were afraid to be seen ; keeping as low as possible for security.*] One of us'll have to take th' risk, an' go for Father Domineer at once. [*He waits for a few moments, but no-one answers.*] Did yous hear me, or are yous lettin' on to be deaf ? I said one of us'll have to go for Father Domineer. [*There is no reply.*] Are you listenin' to me be any chance, Sailor Mahan ?

Mahan. I heard you, I heard you.

Michael. An' why don't you go, then ?

Mahan [*coming down towards Michael — crouching low*]. Nice thing if I met th' Cock barrin' me way ? Why don't you go yourself ?

Michael. What about th' possibility of me meetin' him ? I'm more conspicuous in this disthrict than you, an' th' thing would take immediate recognisance of me.

Sergeant [*coming down towards them — crouching too*]. Me an' Sailor Mahan'll go together.

Michael [*indignantly*]. An' leave me to grapple with *mysteriosa Daemones* alone ? [*He turns his face sky-wards*] Oh, in this disthrict there's not a sign of one willin' to do unto another what another would do to him !

Mahan [*fiercely*]. That's a lie : there isn't a one who isn't eager to do to others what others would do to him !

[*The Bellman, dressed as a fireman, comes in, and walks along on the path outside. He has a huge brass fireman's helmet on his head, and is wearing a red shirt, and blue trousers. He has a bell in his hand which he rings loudly before he shouts his orders. The three men cease their discussion, and give him their full attention.*

Bellman [*shouting*]. Into your houses all ! Bar th' doors, shut th' windows ! Th' Cock's comin' ! In the shape of a woman ! Gallus, Le Coq, an Kyleloch, th' Cock's comin' in th' shape of a woman ! Into your houses, shut to th' windows, bar th' doors !

[*He goes out in the opposite direction, shouting his orders and ringing his bell, leaving the three men agitated and more frightened than ever,*

Sergeant [*frantically*]. Into the house with us all — quick !

Michael [*hindering him — ferociously*]. Not in there, you fool ! Th' house is full o' them. You seen what happened to the whiskey ? If he or she comes, th' thing to do is to take no notice ; if he or she talks, not to answer ; and take no notice of whatever questionable shape it takes. Sit down, quiet, th' three of us.

[*The three men sit down on the ground — Michael to the right, the Sergeant to the left, and Mahan in the centre.*

Michael [*trembling*]. Now, let th' two of yous pull yourselves together. An' you, Mahan, sing that favourite of yours, quietly, as if we were passing th' time pleasantly. [*As Mahan hesitates*] Go on, man, for God's sake !

Mahan [*agitated*]. I can't see how I'll do it justice undher these conditions. I'll thry. [*He sings, but his voice quavers occasionally*] :

Long time ago when men was men
An' ships not ships that sail'd just to an' fro-o-o ;
We hoisted sail an' sail'd, an' then sail'd on an' on to Jericho-o-o ;
With silks an' spice came back again because we'd nowhere else to go !

Michael }
Sergeant } [*together*]. Go, go !

Mahan [*singing*] :

Th' captain says, says he we'll make
Th' pirates where th' palm trees wave an' grow-o-o,
Haul down their sable flag, an' pray, before we hang them all, heave yo-ho-ho ;
Then fling their bodies in th' sea to feed th' fishes down below !

Michael ⎱
Sergeant ⎰ [*together*]. Low, low !

> [*A golden shaft of light streams in from the left of the road,
> and, a moment afterwards, Loreleen appears in the midst
> of it. She stands in the gateway staring at the three men
> squatted on the ground.*

Loreleen [*puzzled*]. What th' hell's wrong here ?

Michael [*in a whisper — motioning Mahan to continue*]. Go
on, man.

Mahan [*singing — with more quavers in his voice*] :

An' when we've swabb'd th' blood away,
We'll take their hundhred-ton gunn'd ship in tow-o-o ;
Their precious jewels'll go to deck th' breasts of women,
    white as snow-o-o ;
So hoist all sail an' make for home through waves that lash
    an' winds that blow !

Michael ⎱
Sergeant ⎰ [*together*]. Blow, blow !

> [*Loreleen comes into the garden, and approaches the men.
> The golden light follows her, and partly shines on the
> three singers.*

Loreleen [*brightly*]. Singin' is it the three of you are ?
Practisin' for the fancy-dress ball tonight, eh ? Ye do
well to bring a spray of light, now and again, into a
dark place. The Sergeant's eyes, too, whenever Lorna
or me passes by, are lit with a light that never was on
sea or land. An' th' bould Sailor Mahan is smiling
too ; only dad is dour. [*She glances at the bottle on the
table.*] The song is heard, th' wine is seen, only th'
women wanting. [*She runs over to the porchway, and
shouts into the house*] Lorna, Marion, come on down,
come out here, an' join th' enthertainment !

[*Lorna and Marion come trotting out of the house into the garden. They are both clad in what would be called fancy dress. Lorna is supposed to be a gypsy, and is wearing a short black skirt, low-cut green bodice, with a gay sash round her waist, sparkling with sequins. Her fair arms are bare. Her head is bound with a silver and black ornament, similar in shape to that already worn by Marion. Her legs are encased in black stockings, and dark-red shoes cover her feet. Marion is dressed as a Nippy, a gay one. She has on a short, bright-green skirt, below which a black petticoat peeps; a low-cut bodice of a darker green, and sports a tiny black apron to protect her costume. She wears light-brown silk stockings, and brown shoes. Outside the white bandeau round her head she wears the ornament worn before. The two women stare at the three men.*]

Lorna [*vexatiously*]. Dhrunk is it? To get in that state just when we were practisin' a few steps for tonight's fancy-dress dance! [*She notices the bottle.*] Looka th' dhrink left out in th' sun an' air to dhry! [*She whips up the bottle, and places it inside on the floor of the porch.*] An' even th' Sailor Mahan is moody too! [*She goes over to the Sergeant, stands behind him, and lays a hand on his head. She is now in the golden light which shines down on the Sergeant too.*]

I saw a ship a-sailing, a-sailing on th' sea;
An' among its spicy cargo was a bonny lad for me!

[*The Sergeant rises slowly, as if enchanted, with a foolish look of devotion on his face, till he stands upright beside Lorna, glancing at her face, now and again, very shy and uncertain. While this has been happening, Loreleen has gone to Sailor Mahan, and now stands behind him with a hand on his head.*]

Loreleen [*down to Sailor Mahan*] :

  I saw a man come running, come running o'er th' lea, sir,
  And, lo, he carried silken gowns
  That couldn't hide a knee
  That he had bought in saucy towns ;
  An' jewels he'd bought beyond th' bounds
  Of Asia's furthest sea.
  And all were lovely, all were fine,
  An' all were meant for me !

  [*Sailor Mahan rises, as if enchanted, till he stands upright
  beside Loreleen, slyly looking at her now and again.*

Marion. Aw, let's be sensible. [*She sees the gun.*] What's
  th' gun doin' ? Who owns th' gun ?

Sergeant. It's mine. I'm on pathrol lookin' to shoot
  down th' demon-bird loose among innocent people.

Marion. Demon-bird loose among innocent people ?
  Yous must be mad.

Sergeant [*indignantly*]. We're not mad ! It's only that we
  were startled when th' darkness came, th' lightning
  flashed, an' we saw Mr. Marthraun's tall-hat turnin'
  itself into th' demon-bird !

Lorna [*mystified*]. Th' darkness came, th' lightning
  flashed ? A tall-hat changin' into a demon-bird !

Michael [*springing to his feet*]. Ay, an' this isn't th' time for
  gay disturbance ! So go in, an' sthrip off them gaudy
  things, an' bend your mind to silent prayer an' long
  fastin' ! Fall prostrate before God, admittin' your
  dire disthress, an' you may be admitted to a new dis-
  pensation !

Lorna [*to Michael*]. Nonsense ! Your new tall-hat was
  delivered an hour ago, an' is upstairs now, waitin' for

                                                        E

you to put it on. [*To Marion*] Take that gun in, dear, outa th' way, an' bring down th' tall-hat to show him he's dhreamin'.

[*Marion takes up the gun, and goes into the house with it, as Michael, in a great rage, shoves Mahan aside to face Lorna fiercely.*

Michael [*loudly*]. Who are you, you jade, to set yourself up against th' inner sight an' outer sight of genuine Christian men? [*He shouts*] We seen this thing, I tell you! If you knew what you ought to know, you'd acknowledge th' thrained tenacity of evil things. Betther had I left you soakin' in poverty, with your rags coverin' your thin legs, an' your cheeks hollow from mean feedin'. Through our bulgin' eyes, didn't we see th' horrification of me tall-hat turnin' into th' demonised cock? Me tall-hat, you bitch, me own tall-hat is roamin' round th' counthry, temptin' souls to desthroy themselves with dancin' an' desultory pleasures!

Mahan [*gripping Michael's arm*]. Aw, draw it mild, Mick!

Michael [*flinging off Mahan's hold*]. Go in, an' take them things, showy with sin, off you, an' dhress decent! [*He points to Loreleen*] It's you who's brought this blast from th' undherworld, England, with you! It's easy seen what you learned while you worked there — a place where no God is; where pride and lust an' money are the brightest liveries of life! [*He advances as if to strike her, but Mahan bars his way.*] You painted slug! [*Marion comes from the house, carrying a fresh, dignified tall-hat, noble in its silken glossiness. She offers it to Michael who jumps away from it.*] No, no, take it away; don't let it touch me.

[*Marion puts the hat on the table, and the three men stare at it, as if expecting something to happen.*

Lorna [*darting into the porch, and returning with the bottle. It has gone back to its former colour*]. Let's have a dhrink to give us courage to fight our dangers. Fetch another glass, Marion.

    [*Marion goes in, and returns with a glass. Lorna uncorks the bottle, and takes up a glass to fill it.*

Michael [*warningly*]. Don't meddle with that dhrink, or harm may come to us all !

Lorna [*recklessly*]. If I can't wrap myself in th' arms of a man, I'll wrap myself in a cordial. [*She fills the glass, then she fills another one, and gives it to Loreleen ; then she fills a third, and gives it to Marion.*] Here, Loreleen. [*Loreleen takes the glass.*] Here, Marion.

    [*Marion takes the glass from her.*

Mahan [*doubtfully, and with some fear*]. I wouldn't, Lorna, I wouldn't dhrink it — there's some kind of a spell on it.

Lorna. Is there, now ? I hope to God it's a strong one ! [*Raising her glass*] Th' Cock-a-doodle Dandy !

Marion ⎱ [*raising their glasses — together*]. Th' Cock-a-doodle
Loreleen ⎰ Dandy !

    [*The three women empty their glasses together. Lorna fills her glass again, and goes over to the Sergeant.*

Lorna [*offering the glass to the Sergeant*]. Dhrink, hearty man, an' praise th' good things life can give. [*As he hesitates*] Dhrink from th' glass touched by th' lips of a very fair lady !

Sergeant [*impulsively*]. Death an' bedamnit, ma'am, it's a fair lady you are. [*He takes the glass from her*] I'm not th' one to be short in salutin' loveliness !

> [*He drinks, and a look of delightful animation gradually comes on to his face.*

Loreleen [*who has filled her glass again — going over to Sailor Mahan, and offering him the drink*]. Here, Sailor Mahan, man of th' wider waters, an' th' seven seas, dhrink ! [*As he hesitates*] Dhrink from th' glass touched by th' lips of a very fair lady !

Mahan [*taking the glass — impulsively*]. Here's a one who always yelled ahoy to a lovely face an' charmin' figure whenever they went sailin' by — *salud* !

> [*He drinks, and the look of animation gradually comes on to his face too.*

Marion [*who has filled her glass the second time — going over to Michael and offering him the drink*]. Dark man, let th' light come to you be dhrinkin' from a glass touched be th' red lips of a fair, young maiden !

Michael [*who has been watching the others enviously — taking the glass from her*]. Gimme it ! I won't be one odd. Yous can't best me ! [*He drinks it down greedily. A reckless looks steals over his face.*]

> [*During the last few moments, Lorna has been humming a tune, which has been taken up by an accordion, very softly. Then the Messenger appears on the pathway outside, and it can be seen that he is the player. He sits sideways on the wall, still playing softly a kind of a dance tune.*

Messenger [*to Marion*]. In our heart of hearts, maid Marion,

we care nothin' about th' world of men. Do we now,
Sailor Mahan ?

Mahan [*cautiously — though a reckless gleam is appearing in
his eyes too*]. We all have to think about th' world o'
men at times.

Michael. Not with our hearts, Sailor Mahan ; oh, not
with our hearts. You're thinkin' now of th' exthra
money you want off me, Sailor Mahan. Take it,
man, an' welcome ! [*Enthusiastically*] An' more ! You
can have double what you're askin', without a whimper,
without a grudge !

Mahan [*enthusiastically*]. No, damnit, Michael, not a
penny from you ! We're as good as bein' brothers !
Looka th' lilies of th' field, an' ask yourself what th'
hell's money !

Michael [*excitedly*]. Dhross, be God ! Dhross, an' nothin'
else ! [*To Marion*] Gimme that hat there !

    [*She gives it to him. He puts it on, puts an arm round her
waist, and they begin to move with the beat of the music.
As Michael puts his arm around her waist, the ornament
on her head rises into a graceful, curving horn, but he
does not notice it.*

    [*At the same time, the Sergeant, having put an arm round
Lorna, moves in the dance, too. As he does so, the ornament on her head, too, becomes a curving horn, but he
does not notice it. Then Mahan goes over stealthily to
Loreleen, who is watching the others, and stabs her shyly
in the ribs with a finger. She turns, smiles, takes hold
of his arm, and puts it round her waist. Then the two
of them join the others in moving round to the beat of the
music, the cock-like crest in Loreleen's hat rising higher
as she begins to move in the dance.*

[*After a few moments, the dance quickens, the excitement grows, and the men stamp out the measure of the music fiercely, while the three women begin to whirl round them with ardour and abandon. While the excitement is at its height, a loud, long peal of thunder is heard, and in the midst of it, with a sliding, rushing pace, Father Domineer appears in the gateway, a green glow enveloping him, as he glares down at the swinging dancers, and as a loud, lusty crow from the Cock rings out through the garden.*]

[*The dancers, excepting Loreleen, suddenly stand stock still, then fall on one knee, facing the priest, their heads bent in shame and some dismay. Loreleen dances on for some few moments longer, the music becoming softer, then she slowly ends her dance to face forward towards the priest, the Messenger continuing to play the tune very softly, very faintly now.*]

Father Domineer [*down to those in the garden — with vicious intensity*]. Stop that devil's dance ! How often have yous been warned that th' avowed enemies of Christianity are on th' march everywhere ! An' I find yous dancin' ! How often have yous been told that pagan poison is floodin' th' world, an' that Ireland is dhrinkin' in generous doses through films, plays, an' books ! An' yet I come here to find yous dancin' ! Dancin', an' with th' Kyleloch, Le Coq, Gallus, th' Cock rampant in th' disthrict, desthroyin' desire for prayer, desire for work, an' weakenin' th' authority of th' pastors an' masters of your souls ! Th' empire of Satan's pushin' out its foundations everywhere, an' I find yous dancin', *ubique ululanti cockalorum ochone, ululo !*

Messenger [*through his soft playing of the accordion*]. Th' devil was as often in th' street, an' as intimate in th' home when there was nor film nor play nor book.

Father Domineer. There was singin' then, an' there's singin' now ; there was dancin' then, an' there's dancin' now, leadin' innocent souls to perjure their perfection. [*To Loreleen*] Kneel down, as th' others do, you proud an' dartin' cheat, an' beg a pardon !

Loreleen [*obstinately*]. I seek no pardon for th' dance that's done.

Father Domineer [*turning away from her*]. Seek for it then when pardon hides away.

Michael. Oh, what have I done ! I've bethrayed meself into a sudden misdoin' !

Mahan. Mea culpa, me, too, Father !

Father Domineer. Oh, Michael Marthraun, an' you, Sailor Mahan, knights of Columbanus, I come to help yous, an' I catch yous in th' act of prancin' about with shameless women, dhressed to stun th' virtue out of all beholdhers !

Michael. It was them, right enough, Father, helped be th' wine, that done poor me an' poor Sailor Mahan in ! I should have remembered that a Columbanian knight told me a brother Columbanian knight told him another brother has said that St. Jerome told a brother once that woman was th' gate of hell ! An' it's thrue — they stab a man with a knife wreathed with roses !

Father Domineer. Get up, get up, an' stand away from me ; an' let ye never be loungers again in th' fight for good against evil. [*They all rise up humbly, the women to one side, the men to the other, and go back some way, as the Priest comes into the garden. Loreleen strolls defiantly over to the table, and sits sideways upon it. To Mahan*] An' now,

Sailor Mahan, a special word for you. On my way here, I passed that man of yours who's livin' in sin with a lost an' wretched woman. He dodged down a lane to give me th' slip. I warned you, if he didn't leave her, to dismiss him — did you do so? [*Mahan is silent.*] I have asked you, Mahan, if you've dismissed him?

Mahan [*obstinately*]. I see no reason why I should dismiss me best lorry driver.

Father Domineer [*coldly*]. You don't see a reason? An' who are you to have any need of a reason in a question of this kind? [*Loudly*] I have a reason, an' that's enough for you!

Mahan [*defensively*]. He's a fine worker, Father, an' th' nation needs such as him.

Father Domineer [*loudly*]. We're above all nations. Nationality is mystical, maundering nonsense! It's a heresy! I'm the custodian of higher interests. [*Shouting*] Do as you're told — get rid of him!

Michael [*wheedling*]. It's all right, Father — he'll do what your reverence tells him. Sailor Mahan's a thrue Columbanian.

Mahan [*angrily — to Michael*]. He won't do what his reverence tells him!

[*Down the path outside comes the Lorry Driver, a man of thirty years of age. He doesn't look a giant, but there is an air of independence and sturdiness about him. He is wearing a leather jacket, a pair of soldier's khaki trousers, and an oily-looking peaked cap. His face is tanned by the weather, and his upper lip is hidden by a well-trimmed moustache. He hesitates for a moment when*] *he sees Father Domineer; but, stiffening a little, he continues his walk to the gateway, into the garden. He stands a little way from Mahan, looking at him, evidently having something to say to him.*

Father Domineer [*sneeringly*]. Ah, the gentleman himself has arrived. [*To the man*] We were just talking of you, my man. I have told Mr. Mahan to dismiss you. You know why. You're a scandal to th' whole place; you're a shame to us all. Either leave this woman you're living with, or go to where that sort of thing's permitted. [*Loudly*] You heard me?

Lorry Driver [*surlily*]. I heard you.

Father Domineer [*impatiently*]. Well?

Lorry Driver. I come to speak with Mr. Mahan, Father.

Mahan [*quickly*]. Me, Jack! Oh, yes; what's the throuble now?

Lorry Driver. Plenty, sir. The turf-workers have left th' bog, an' we've no turf to load. Th' delegate says he sent a telegram to Mr. Marthraun, sayin' th' men would leave th' bog, if no answer came within an hour.

Messenger. He did, an' I delivered it.

Michael. Damnit, but I forgot about it! The tension here put it out of me mind!

Father Domineer [*catching the Lorry Driver by an arm*]. Never mind turf or tension now. Are you going to go from here?

Lorry Driver [*obstinately*]. I'll go, if Mr. Mahan tells me to go.

Father Domineer [*in a fury*]. Isn't it a wondher God doesn't strike you dead ! I tell you to give the wretched woman up, or go, an' that's enough for either Sailor Mahan or you. [*He shakes the Lorry Driver's arm.*] Will you give that wretched woman up ; will you send that woman of yours away ?

Lorry Driver [*resentfully*]. Eh, don't be pullin' th' arm outa me !

Father Domineer [*his fury growing*]. Did you send that woman away ; are you going to do it ?

Lorry Driver [*shaking his arm free, and stepping back*]. Aw, let go ! I didn't an' I won't !

Father Domineer [*in an ungovernable burst of fury*]. You wretch, would you dare to outface your priest ? Get out of me sight !

> [*He lunges forward, and strikes the Lorry Driver swiftly and savagely on the side of the head. The man falls heavily ; lies still for a moment ; tries feebly to rise ; falls down again, and lies quite still.*

Mahan [*frightened*]. He's hurted, Father ; you hot him far too hard.

Father Domineer [*frightened too — with a forced laugh*]. Nonsense ! I just touched him. [*He touches the fallen man with his foot.*] Get up, get up — you're not that much hurt.

Mahan [*bending over the Lorry Driver, and placing a hand on his breast*]. I'm afraid he's either dyin' or dead, Father !

> [*Father Domineer runs over agitatedly to the fallen man, kneels down beside him, and murmurs in his ear. Then he raises his head to face the others.*

Father Domineer [*to the others*]. Yous all saw what happened. I just touched him, an' he fell. I'd no intention of hurting him — only to administer a rebuke.

Sergeant [*consolingly*]. Sure, we know that, Father — it was a pure accident.

Father Domineer. I murmured an act of contrition into th' poor man's ear.

Messenger [*playing very softly*]. It would have been far fitther, Father, if you'd murmured one into your own.

END OF SCENE II

It is towards dusk in the garden now. The sun is setting, and the sky shows it. The rich blue of the sky has given place to a rich yellow, slashed with green and purple. The flag-pole stands black against the green and yellow of the sky, and the flag, now, has the same sombre hue.

The big sunflowers against the wall have turned into a solemn black, too ; the house has a dark look, save where a falling shaft from the sun turns the window above the porch into a golden eye of light. Far away, in the depths of the sky, the evening star can be faintly seen.

In the distance, for some time, the sounds of drumming, occasionally pierced by the shrill notes of a fife, can be heard.

Mahan is sitting at the table, busy totting up figures on papers spread out before him, his face knotted into creases of anxiety and doubt.

Lorna and Marion are leaning against the wall, away from the gateway, and near the house. Their gay garments are covered with dark hooded cloaks to temper the coolness of the evening air.

Lorna. They all seem to be out on th' hunt — police an' soldiers, with th' bands to give them courage. Th' fools !

Marion. D'ye think they'll get him ? Th' place'll lose its brightness if th' Cock's killed.

Lorna. How can they desthroy a thing they say them-selves is not of this world ? [*She goes over to Mahan, and stares at him for a moment.*] It's cooler. The sun's settin'.

Mahan [*hardly noticing*]. Is it ? I didn't notice. I'm busy. Everything thrust through everything else, since that damned Cock got loose. Th' drouth now dhryin' everything to dust ; the turf-workers refusin' to work, th' women thinkin' only of dancin' an' dhress. But we'll lay him low, an' bury him deep enough to forget he ever came here !

Lorna. Th' men on th' bog work hard ; they should get all you've got to give them.

Mahan [*resentfully*]. An' why th' hell shouldn't they work hard ? Who'd keep th' fires of th' nation burning, if they didn't ?

Lorna. They work for you, too ; an' for Michael. He's got a pile in th' bank, an' rumour says you've got one too.

Mahan [*whining*]. Michael may ; I never had, an' I'm losin' th' little I had since I lost me best lorry dhriver — blast th' hand that hot him !

    [*The Cock suddenly glides in, weaving a way between Mahan at the table, and Lorna, circling the garden, and finally disappearing round the gable-end of the house ; the dance tune softly keeps time with his movements. Jumping to his feet*] What was that ? I thought I saw him prancin' by me !

Lorna [*startled too*]. What was what ?

Mahan. Th' Cock in his black plumage, yellow legs, an' crimson crest !

Marion [*who has gone tense*]. You put th' heart across me ! I thought you meant th' poor dead man.
                [*She turns to look along the road again.*

Lorna [*to Mahan*]. There's little use worryin' over figures till you settle with th' men.

Mahan [*irritably*]. That's Mick's business, that's Mick's business !

Marion [*running over to whisper excitedly to Lorna*]. Here they are — Father Domineer an' Mr. Marthraun comin' along th' road !

Mahan [*irascibly*]. Aw, what does that Father Domineer want comin' here when we've so much to think about ! Delayin' things ! I want to get away from here before it gets dark.

Lorna. Didn't you know they're goin' to purge th' poor house of its evil influences ?

Mahan [*irritably*]. Oh, can't they do first things first ?

[*Along the pathway outside come Father Domineer and Michael, followed by a lad. The lad is One-eyed Larry. His face is one alternately showing stupidity or cunning, according to whomsoever may be speaking to him. Where his left eye was is a black cavity, giving him a somewhat sinister look. He is lanky and rather awkward-looking. He is wearing a black cassock or soutane, piped with red braid, and is bare-headed. He is carrying a small bell, a book, and an unlighted candle. He shuffles along after the two men, and follows them into the garden.*]

Father Domineer. We'll banish them, never fear, Michael, before I have to leave th' parish because of that unhappy accident. I've faced worse. Be staunch. Th' bell is powerful, so is th' book, an' th' blessed candle, too. [*He glances at the women.*] Let yous women keep to th' farther end of th' garden. [*He glances at Mahan.*] We won't be long, Sailor Mahan. [*Suddenly, as he,*

Michael, and One-eyed Larry reach the porch] Where's that other one ?

Michael. Is it Loreleen, me daughter, Father ?

Father Domineer. She's no daughter of yours, Michael. [*Bending down to whisper warningly*] Get rid of her, get rid of her — she's dangerous !

Michael. How get rid of her, Father ?

Father Domineer. Pack her off to America !

Michael [*respectfully — as they are about to go into the house*]. I'll go first, Father.

Father Domineer [*setting him gently aside*]. No, no ; mine th' gap of danger.

> [*The three of them go in, the Priest first, then Michael, and, lastly, One-eyed Larry. Marion and Lorna move over to the farther side of the garden.*

Lorna. It's all damn nonsense, though Michael has me nerves in such a way that I'm near ready to believe in anything.

Mahan. Waste of time, too. It'll take a bhetter man than Father Domineer to dhrive evil things outa Eire.

Marion. Messenger says he's only addin' to their number, an' soon a noddin' daffodil, when it dies, 'll know its own way to hell. [*The roll of a drum is heard and a great boo-ing. Marion runs to the wall to look over it, and up the road.* [*Excitedly*] A girl runnin' this way, hell for leather. My God, it's Loreleen !

> [*After a few moments, Loreleen runs along the pathway outside, and dashes in through the gateway to Lorna, who catches her in her arms. Clumps of grass and sods of*

turf, and a few stones follow Loreleen in her rush along the road.

Loreleen [*out of breath*]. God damn th' dastards of this vile disthrict ! They pelted me with whatever they could lay hands on — th' women because they couldn't stand beside me ; th' men because there was ne'er a hope of usin' me as they'd like to ! Is it any wondher that th' girls are fleein' in their tens of thousands from this bewildhered land ? Blast them ! I'll still be gay an' good-lookin'. Let them draw me as I am not, an' sketch in a devil where a maiden stands !

Lorna [*soothingly*]. Be calm, child ! We can't go in, for Father Domineer's inside puttin' things in ordher. [*Releasing Loreleen*] I'll run along th' road to them disturbers, an' give them a bit o' me mind ! [*She catches hold of Marion's arm*] Come on, Marion !
 [*She and Marion rush out along the road, and pass out of sight.*]

Loreleen [*staring at the house*]. He's inside, is he ? That's not where th' evil is, th' gaum, if he wants to know.

Mahan [*seriously*]. Come here, Loreleen ; nearer, for I've something to say to you. [*As she does not stir, he grips her arm, and draws her farther from the house.*] We might be heard.

Loreleen [*suspiciously*]. What do you want, Sailor Mahan ? You're not of one mind with them who chased me ?

Mahan [*a little embarrassed*]. Aw, God, no ! Me sails of love are reefed at last, an' I lie quiet, restin' in a lonely harbour now. I'm too old to be flusthered with that kinda folly. I just want to warn you to get outa this disthrict.

Loreleen [*bitterly*]. Why must I go? Is it because I'm good-lookin' an' gay?

   [*But the bold Mahan isn't indifferent to the charms of Loreleen. So he goes on to show Loreleen the youthfulness of his old age; that his muscles are still strong, his fibres flexible. He becomes restless, and walks about, occasionally glancing at the house, nervous at what may be happening inside. When he comes to a chair, he non-chalantly swings a leg over the back of it, turning on the foot of the same leg to swing the other one back again. These actions, like the conversation, though not done in a hurry, are done quickly, as if he wanted to say all he had to say before any interruption.*

Mahan [*swinging a leg over a chair*]. Partly because you're good-lookin' an' partly because of th' reckless way you talk. Remember what happened to poor Jack. I'd clear out if I were you.

   [*He vaults on to the table, swings round it on his backside, and vaults from it on the opposite side, a little stiffly.*

Loreleen. How'm I to clear out? I've no money left. Th' forty pounds I had, Dad put into his bank for me, an' now won't give me a penny of it, because he says if I got it, I'd go to England; an' if I went to England, I'd lose me soul, th' shaky, venomous lout! An' I keep quiet because of Lorna. [*Hurriedly, as Mahan is stiffly climbing a few feet up the flag-pole*] Oh, don't be doin' th' monkey on a stick! Maybe you could help me? Could you, would you?

Mahan [*sliddering from the pole, swinging a leg over a chair, and coming closer to her*]. Now that's what I'd hoped you'd say. This is th' first time I've caught you alone. I'll give you what you need, an' you can weigh anchor,

F

an' be off outa this damned place.   Listen, darlin' :
you steal out tonight to th' Red Barn, west of th' Holy
Cross, an' I'll dhrive there with what'll get you as far
as you want to go.   [*He suddenly puts an arm round her in
a kind of clutch.*]   Jasus, you have lovely eyes !

Loreleen [*trying to pull his arm away*].   Oh, Sailor Mahan,
don't do that !   Let me go — someone may see us !

Mahan [*recklessly*].   You deserve to be ruffled a bit !   Well,
will you come to th' Red Barn, while th' rest are goin'
to th' dance, an' save yourself ?   Yes or no !

Loreleen.   Maybe, maybe ;   yes, yes, I'll go.   Let go your
clutch !

> [*The house shakes ;   a sound of things moving and crockery
> breaking comes from it ;   several flashes of lightning spear
> out through the window over the porch ;   and the flag-pole
> wags drunkenly from side to side.*
>
> [*Marion and Lorna appear on the pathway outside the wall,
> and hurry along into the garden just as One-eyed Larry
> comes running out of the house, his face beset with fear.
> His one eye takes in the picture of Loreleen breaking away
> from Mahan.   Loreleen turns aside from One-eyed Larry,
> while Mahan, embarrassed, turns to face him.*

One-eyed Larry [*excitedly*].   It's startin' in earnest !   There's
a death-sthruggle goin' on in there !   Poor Father
Domineer's got a bad black eye, an' Micky Marthraun's
coat is torn to tatthers !

Lorna [*hurrying into the garden*].   What's happened, what's
happenin' ?

Mahan [*with dignity — to One-eyed Larry*].   Misther Marthraun in your mouth, me lad.

Loreleen [*mischievously*]. Let th' lad tell his funny story.

One-eyed Larry [*turning on Loreleen*]. It's funny to you because you're in league with th' evil ones ! [*To the others*] One o' Father Domineer's feet is all burned be a touch from one o' them, an' one o' Mickey's is frozen stiff be a touch from another. [*To Mahan*] Maybe you'd ha' liked me to have lost me other eye while you were warmin' yourself in that one's arms !

[*He points to Loreleen.*

Mahan [*furiously*]. You one-eyed get, if you had two, I'd cyclonise you with a box !

Loreleen [*unmoved — a little mockingly*]. An' how did th' poor lamb lose his eye ?

Mahan [*indifferently*]. Oh, when he was a kid, he was hammerin' a bottle, an' a flyin' piece cut it out of his head.

One-eyed Larry [*venomously*]. You're a liar, that wasn't th' way ! It was th' Demon Cock who done it to me. Only certain eyes can see him, an' I had one that could. He caught me once when I was spyin' on him, put a claw over me left eye, askin' if I could see him then ; an' on me sayin' no, put th' claw over th' other one, an' when I said I could see him clear now, says he, that eye sees too well, an' on that, he pushed an' pushed till it was crushed into me head.

Loreleen [*mockingly*]. What a sad thing to happen.

[*The house shakes worse than before, and seems to lurch over to one side. The flag-pole wags from side to side merrily ; there is a rumble of thunder, and blue lightning flashes from the window. All, except Loreleen, cower together at the far end of the garden. She stands over by the wall, partly framed by the sable sunflowers.*

Marion [*full of fright*]. Sacred Heart ! Th' house'll fall asundher !

Loreleen [*gleefully*]. Let it ! It's th' finest thing that could happen to it !

One-eyed Larry [*trembling violently*]. It's now or never for them an' for us. They're terrible powerful spirits. Knocked th' bell outa me hand, blew out th' candle, an' tore th' book to threads ! Thousands of them there are, led be th' bigger ones — Kissalass, Velvethighs, Reedabuck, Dancesolong, an' Sameagain. Keep close. Don't run. They might want help. [*Screeches like those of barn owls are heard from the house, with the " too-whit too-whoo " of other kinds, the cackling of hens, and the loud cawing of crows. Frantically pushing his way to the back of the others*] Oooh ! Let me get back, get back !

[*The house shakes again ; the flag-pole totters and falls flat ; blue and red lightning flashes from the window, and a great peal of thunder drums through the garden. Then all becomes suddenly silent. They all hang on to each other, shivering with fear, except Loreleen, who lights a cigarette, puts a foot on a chair, leans on its back, looks at the house, and smokes away serenely.*

Lorna [*tremulously*]. Why has th' house gone so silent suddenly ?

One-eyed Larry [*from the rear*]. They've either killed th' demons, or th' demons has killed them.

Marion. God save us, they must be dead !

Loreleen [*with quiet mockery*]. Welcome be th' will o' God.

Lorna [*suddenly — with great agitation*]. Get back, get back !
Run ! There's something comin' out !

> [*She, Marion, and One-eyed Larry race for the gateway,
> rush on to the sidewalk, and bend down, so that only their
> heads can be seen peeping over the wall. Mahan shrinks
> back to the far end of the garden, and Loreleen remains
> where she is.*

> [*From the house, sideways, through the now lurching porch,
> come Father Domineer and Michael. Both are limping,
> Father Domineer on his left foot, Michael on his right one.
> Domineer has a big black eye, his coat is awry on his
> back, and his hair is widely tossed. Michael's coat hangs
> in tatters on him. Father Domineer's face is begrimed
> with the smudges of smoke, and both look tired, but elated.*

> [*One-eyed Larry at once runs out, and takes his place
> reverently behind them, standing with his hands folded
> piously in front of his breast, his eyes bent towards the
> ground. Mahan straightens up, and Lorna and Marion
> return to the garden. Loreleen remains as she was.*

Father Domineer [*as he enters with Michael*]. Be assured, good
people, all's well, now. The house is safe for all. The
evil things have been banished from the dwelling.
Most of the myrmidons of Anticlericus, Secularius, an'
Odeonius, have been destroyed. The Civic Guard and
the soldiers of Feehanna Fawl will see to the few who
escaped. We can think quietly again of our Irish
Sweep. Now I must get to my car to go home, and have
a wash an' brush up. (*To Marion and Lorna*] Off you go
into the house, good women. Th' place, th' proper
place, th' only place for th' woman. Straighten it out,
and take pride in doing it. [*He shoves Marion towards the
porch*] Go on, woman, when you're told ! [*To Michael*]

You'll have to exert your authority more as head of the house.

Michael [*asserting it at once — to Lorna*]. You heard what Father Domineer said. Go on ; in you go, an' show yourself a decent, God-fearin' woman.

Father Domineer [*trying to be gracious — to Lorna*]. Th' queen of th' household as th' husband is th' king.

    [*Marion has gone into the house with a sour-looking face, and Lorna now follows her example, looking anything but charmed.*

Father Domineer [*turning to Loreleen*]. And you — aren't you going in to help ?

Loreleen [*quietly*]. No, thanks ; I prefer to stay on in the garden.

Father Domineer [*thunderously*]. Then learn to stand on the earth in a more modest and suitable way, woman ! [*Pointing to ornaments on crest of hat and breast of bodice*] An' do you mind that th' ornaments ye have on of brooch an' bangle were invented be th' fallen angels, now condemned to everlastin' death for worshippin' beauty that faded before it could be clearly seen ? [*Angrily*] Oh, woman, *de cultus feminarum malifico eradicum !*

Michael. That one's mind is always mustherin' dangerous thoughts plundered outa evil books !

Father Domineer [*startled*]. Books ? What kinda books ? Where are they ?

Michael. She has some o' them in th' house this minute.

Father Domineer [*roaring*]. Bring them out, bring them out ! How often have I to warn you against books ! Hell's bells tolling people away from th' thruth! Bring them out, *in annem fiat ecclesiam nonsensio*, before th' demoneens we've banished flood back into th' house again!

[*Michael and One-eyed Larry jostle together into the porch and into the house to do Father Domineer's bidding.*

Loreleen [*taking her leg down from the chair, and striding over to Father Domineer*]. You fool, d'ye know what you're thryin' to do? You're thryin' to keep God from talkin'!

Father Domineer. You're speakin' blasphemy, woman!

Mahan. What do people want with books? I don't remember readin' a book in me life.

[*Michael comes back carrying a book, followed by One-eyed Larry carrying another. Father Domineer takes the book from Michael, and glances at the title-page.*

Father Domineer [*explosively*]. A book about Voltaire! [*To Loreleen*] This book has been banned, woman.

Loreleen [*innocently*]. Has it now? If so, I must read it over again.

Father Domineer [*to One-eyed Larry*]. What's th' name of that one?

One-eyed Larry [*squinting at the title*]. Ullisississies, or something.

Father Domineer. Worse than th' other one. [*He hands his to One-eyed Larry*] Bring th' two o' them down to th' Presbytery, an' we'll desthroy them. [*Loreleen snatches the two books from One-eyed Larry. One-eyed Larry tries to prevent her, but a sharp push from her sends him toppling over. Loreleen, with great speed, darts out of the gateway, runs along*

*the pathway, and disappears.   Standing as if stuck to the
ground*] Afther her, afther her !

Michael [*astonished*]. Me legs won't move !

Mahan
One-eyed Larry } [*together*]. Nor mine, neither.

> [*As Loreleen disappears, the Cock suddenly springs over the
> wall, and pirouettes in and out between them as they
> stand stuck to the ground.*

> [*Cute ears may hear the quick tune, played softly, of an
> accordion, as the Cock weaves his way about.   The
> Sergeant appears running outside, stops when he sees the
> Cock, leans over the wall, and presents a gun at Michael.*

Michael [*frantically — to Sergeant*]. Not me, man, not me !

> [*Terribly excited, the Sergeant swings the gun till it is
> pointing at Mahan.*

Mahan [*frantically*]. Eh, not me, man !

> [*After the Cock has pirouetted round for some moments,
> while they all remain transfixed, the scene suddenly goes
> dark, though the music continues to sound through it.
> Then two squib-like shots are heard, followed by a clash of
> thunder, and, when the garden enjoys the light of early
> dusk again, which comes immediately after the clap of
> thunder, the music as suddenly ceases.*

> [*The returning light shows that Father Domineer is not
> there ; that Michael and Mahan are stretched out on the
> ground ; and that One-eyed Larry is half over the wall,
> his belly on it, his legs trailing into the garden, his head
> and shoulders protruding into the road.*

Michael [*moaning*]. Shot through the soft flesh an' th'
hard bone !

Mahan [*groaning*]. Shot through th' hard bone an' th' soft flesh !

One-eyed Larry [*shouting*]. Mrs. Marthraun, Marion, we're all killed be th' Cock an' th' Sergeant !
[*Lorna and Marion come running out of the house over to the two prostrate men.*

Lorna. What's happened ?   Where's th' Sergeant ?

One-eyed Larry [*sliddering over the wall, frantic with fear*]. I seen him runnin' off when he'd shot us all !   I'm goin' home, I'm going' home !   Father Domineer's been carried off be th' Demon Cock — I'm off !
[*He runs swiftly down the road, and disappears.*

Lorna [*bending over Michael*]. Where were you hit ?   D'ye think there's a chance of you dyin' ?

Michael [*despairingly*]. I'm riddled !

Lorna [*feeling his body over*]. I can't see a speck of damage on you anywhere, you fool.

Marion [*who has been examining Mahan*]. No, nor on this fella either.

Michael. I tell you th' bullet careered through me breast an' came out be me back !

Mahan. An' then tore through me back an' came out be me breast !

Lorna. What darkness was One-eyed Larry talkin' about ?   An' Father Domineer carried off be the Cock !   Me nerves are all gettin' shatthered.   It's all very thryin'. [*She pokes Michael roughly with her foot.*]   Here, get up, th' both of yous.   There isn't a thing wrong with either of you.

Mahan [*sitting up cautiously, and feeling in his breast pocket*].
What th' hell's this ? [*He pulls out a bullet bigger than a
cigar.*] Looka, Michael Marthraun, th' size of th'
bullet that went tearin' through you an' then through
me ! [*Very devoutly*] Good angels musta gone along
with it, healin' all at th' same time that it tore our
vitals.

Michael [*as devoutly*]. Some higher an' special power musta
been watchin' over us, Sailor Mahan. Sharin' a
miracle, now, Sailor Mahan, we're more than brothers.

Mahan [*fervently*]. We are that, now ; we are indeed.
I'll keep this bullet till th' day I die as a momento of a
mementous occasion !

Lorna [*impatiently*]. Get up, get up. An' don't disturb
us again while we're practisin' for the fancy-dhress
dance tonight in th' hope of winning a spot prize.

Michael [*furiously to her*]. You'll win no spot prize, an'
there'll be no dance till that Demon Cock's laid low !
[*To Mahan — piously*] Thrue men we are, workin' in a
thruly brotherly way for th' good of th' entire community — aren't we, Sailor Mahan ? That's what
saved us !

Mahan [*as piously*]. We are that, Michael ; we are indeed ;
especially now that we've settled th' question finally
so long disputed between us.

Michael [*suspiciously, a note of sharpness in his voice*]. How
settled it ?

Mahan. Be you arrangin' to give me, not only what I was
askin', but twice as much.

Michael [*sarcastically*]. Oh, did I now ? That was damned

good of me ! [*Angrily*] No, nor what you were askin'
either.   D'ye want me to ruin meself to glorify you ?
An' didn't I hear a certain man promisin', nearly on
his oath, he'd give his lorries for next to nothin' to
serve th' community ?

Mahan [*shouting*]. When I was undher a spell, fosthered on
me here ! I'm goin', I'm goin.' I'll argue no more !
[*He goes out by the gate and along the road, pausing as he is
about to disappear.*] For th' last time, Michael Marthraun,
are you goin' to do th' decent for th' sake of th' nation,
an' give me what I'm askin' ?

Michael [*with decision — quietly*]. No, Sailor Mahan, I'm
not. [*He shouts*] I'd see you in hell first !

Mahan [*as he goes*]. A sweet goodbye to you, an' take a
dhrug to keep from stayin' awake o' nights thinkin' of
the nation's needs !

Lorna [*persuasively*]. Be reasonable, Michael.   You're
makin' enough now to be well able to give him all he
asks.

Michael [*savagely seizing her arm*]. Listen, you : even
though you keep th' accounts for me, it's a law of
nature an' a law of God that a wife must be silent
about her husband's secrets !   D'ye hear me, you
costumed slut ?

Lorna [*freeing herself with an effort*]. Don't tear th' arm
out of me ! If you want to embalm yourself in money,
you won't get me to do it !

[*The sound of the wind rising is heard now — a long,
sudden gust-like sound, causing Michael to do a sudden
rush towards the gate, pressing himself back all the time,*

*and gripping the wall when he gets to it. The two women
do not notice the wind.*

Michael. Jasus ! that was a sudden blast !

Lorna [*wondering*]. Blast ? I felt no blast.

Marion [*shaking her head*]. He's undher a spell again.

> [*One-eyed Larry comes running along the road outside,
> excited and shouting. He is holding on tensely to the
> waist-band of his trousers.*

One-eyed Larry [*without the wall*]. A miracle, a miracle !
Father Domineer outa th' darkness, was snatched from
th' claws of the Demon Cock, an' carried home safe on
th' back of a white duck !

Lorna [*amazed*]. On th' back of a white duck ? When
will wondhers cease ! They're all goin' mad !

Michael [*clapping his hands*]. Grand news ! Was it a wild-
duck, now, or merely a domestic one ?

One-eyed Larry. Wild or tame, what does it matther ? It
carried him cheerily through th' sky, an' deposited him
dacently down on his own doorstep !

Michael [*with deep thought*]. It might well have been one
of me own sensible ducks that done it.

One-eyed Larry [*coming to the gate*]. Wait till I tell yous.
Th' Demon Cock's furious at his escape, an' he's
causin' consthernation. He's raised a fierce wind be
th' beat of his wings, an' it's tossin' cattle on to their
backs ; whippin' th' guns from th' hands of Civic
Guard an' soldier, so that th' guns go sailin' through
th' sky like cranes ; an' th' wind's tearin' at the clothes

of th' people. It's only be hard holdin' that I can keep me own trousers on !

Michael [*eagerly*] Th' wind near whipped me on to th' road a minute ago.

[*The Bellman enters on the pathway outside, and meets One-eyed Larry at the gateway, so that the two of them stand there, the one on the left, the other to the right of it.*

[*The collar and one arm are all that are left of the Bellman's coat, and his shirt has been blown outside of his trousers. He is still wearing the brass hat. His right hand is gripping his waist-band, and his left carries the bell that he is ringing.*

Bellman [*shouting*]. Get out, get in ! Th' Demon Cock's scourin' th' skies again, mettlesome, menacin', mol-estifyin' monsther ! Fly to your houses, fall upon your knees, shut th' doors, close th' windows ! In a tearin' rage, he's rippin' th' clouds outa th' sky, because Father Domineer was snatched away from him, an' carried home, fit an' well, on th' back of a speckled duck !

One-eyed Larry [*startled into anger*]. You're a liar, it wasn't a speckled duck ! What are you sayin', fella ? It was a pure white duck that carried th' Father home !

Bellman [*angrily — to One-eyed Larry*]. Liar yourself, an' you're wrong ! It was a speckled duck that done it ; speckled in black, brown, an' green spots. I seen it with me own two eyes doin' th' thrick.

One-eyed Larry [*vehemently*]. I seen it with me one eye in concentration, an' it was a duck white as th' dhriven snow that brought him to his domiceel.

Lorna. I'd say white's a sensible colour, an' more apter for th' job.

Michael. I'd say a speckled duck would look more hand-some landin' on a doorstep than a white fowl.

Marion [*thoughtfully*]. I wondher, now, could it have been Mr. McGilligan's tame barnacle goose ?

Michael [*explosively*]. No, it couldn't have been Mr. McGilligan's tame barnacle goose ! Don't be thryin' to scatther confusion over a miracle happenin' before our very eyes !

[*The Sergeant comes rushing in along the pathway out-side the wall, and runs into the garden through the gate-way, roughly shoving the Bellman and One-eyed Larry out of his way. His cap is gone, a piece of rope is tied round his chest to keep his coat on ; and, when he reaches the gate, all can see that he wears no trousers, leaving him in a long shirt over short pants. He is excited, and his face is almost convulsed with fear and shame.*]

Sergeant [*shoving One-eyed Larry and Bellman aside*]. Outa me way, you fools ! [*Rushing into the garden — to Michael*] Give me one of your oul' trousers, Mick, for th' love o' God ! Whipped off me be a blast of th' wind me own were. When I seen them goin', me entire nature was galvanised into alarmin' anxiety as to what might happen next.

Michael A terrible experience ! What's to come of us, at all !

Sergeant [*tearfully*]. Why isn't Father Domineer here to help ? He doesn't care a damn now, since he was carried home, safe an' sound on th' back of a barnacle goose !

One-eyed Larry [*dumbfounded and angry*]. A barnacle goose ? What are you sayin', man ? It was a dazzlin' white duck that brought him home.

Bellman [*to One-eyed Larry*]. I'm tellin' you it was a specially speckled duck that done it.

Sergeant [*emphatically*]. It was a goose, I'm sayin'. Th' Inspector seen it through a field-glass, an' identified it as a goose, a goose !

Lorna [*amused — laying a hand on Marion's shoulder*]. Look at him, Marion. All dollied up for th' fancy-dhress dance !

Marion [*hilariously*]. It's lookin' like th' blue bonnets are over th' bordher !

Michael [*angrily — to the Sergeant*]. Get into th' house, man, an' don't be standin' there in that style of half-naked finality ! You'll find some oul' trousers upstairs. [*Turning on Lorna and Marion as the Sergeant trots timidly into the house*] You two hussies, have yous no semblance of sense of things past an' things to come ? Here's a sweet miracle only afther happenin', an' there yous are, gigglin' an' gloatin' at an aspect in a man that should send th' two of yous screamin' away ! Yous are as bad as that one possessed, th' people call me daughter.

[*The sound of the wind now rises, swifter, shriller, and stronger, carrying in it an occasional moan, as in a gale, and with this stronger wind comes the Messenger, saunter-ing along outside the wall, sitting down on it when he reaches the end farthest from the house. Nothing in the garden is moved by the wind's whistling violence, except Michael, the Bellman, and One-eyed Larry (who have been suddenly hustled into the garden by the wind*).

*These three now grip their waist-bands, and begin to
make sudden movements to and fro, as if dragged by an
invisible force ; each of them trying to hold back as the
wind pushes them forward. The Messenger is coaxing a
soft tune from his accordion ; while Marion and Lorna
are unaffected by the wind, and stand staring at the men,
amused by their antics.*

Michael [*a little frantic*]. Listen to th' risin' evil of th'
wind ! Oh, th' beat of it, oh, th' beat of it ! We
know where it comes from — red wind on our backs,
black wind on our breasts, thryin' to blow us to hell !

Bellman [*gliding about, pushed by the wind ; holding on to his
trousers with one hand, while he rings his bell with the other
one*]. Fly into th' houses, close th' windows, shut th'
doors !

One-eyed Larry [*gliding in opposite direction*]. We can't, we
can't — we go where th' wind blows us !

Messenger. What ails yous ? I feel only th' brisk breeze
carrying the smell of pinewoods, or th' softer one
carryin' th' scent of th' ripenin' apples.

Michael [*to the women, while he holds fast to his waist-band*].
Get in, an' sthrip off them coloured deceits, smellin'
of th' sly violet an' th' richer rose, sequestherin' a lure
in every petal ! Off with them, I say, an' put on a
cautious grey, or th' stated humbleness of a coal-black
gown ! [*The Sergeant comes from the house wearing Michael's
best black Sunday trousers. He comes from the porch shyly,
but the moment he steps into the garden, his face flashes into a
grim look, and he grabs hold of the waistband, and glides
about as the others do. Seeing the trousers — with a squeal
of indignation*] Me best Sunday black ones ! Couldn't

your damned plundherin' paws pounce on something a
little lowlier to wear ?

Bellman. Get into th' houses, shut to th' doors, close th'
windows !

[*Father Domineer suddenly appears on the pathway outside,
and stands at the gateway looking into the garden. A gust
of wind, fierce and shrill, that preceded him, declines in a
sad wail, and ceases altogether, leaving a sombre silence
behind it. Father Domineer's hair is tossed about ; he
has a wild look in his eyes, and he carries a walking-stick
to help him surmount the limp from the hurt he got when
warring with the evil spirits.*

Father Domineer [*stormily*]. Stop where yous are !   No
hidin' from the enemy !   Back to hell with all bad
books, bad plays, bad pictures, and bad thoughts !
Cock o' th' north, or cock o' th' south, we'll down
derry doh down him yet.   Shoulder to shoulder, an'
step together against th' onward rush of paganism !
Boldly tread, firm each foot, erect each head !

One-eyed Larry
Michael
Bellman   } [*together — very feebly*]. Hurraah !
Sergeant

Father Domineer. Fixed in front be every glance, forward
at th' word advance !

One-eyed Larry
Michael
Bellman   } [*together — very feebly*]. Advance !
Sergeant

Father Domineer. We know where we're goin', an' we
know who's goin' with us.

Michael. The minsthrel boy with th' dear harp of his country, an' Brian O'Lynn.

Bellman. Danny Boy an' th' man who sthruck O'Hara.

One-eyed Larry. Not forgettin' Mick McGilligan's daughter, Maryann !

> [*Sounds of fifing and drumming are heard, mingled with the sound of boo-ing, a little distance away.*

Father Domineer [*jubilantly*]. Listen to th' band ! We're closin' in ; we're winnin' ! [*He puts a hand up to shade his eyes, and peers forward.*] They've collared one of them ! Aha, a woman again ! [*A pause.*] A fine, familiar one too. [*He shouts*] Lead th' slut here, Shanaar, right here in front of me !

> [*He goes through the gateway, and waits in the garden for things to come.*

> [*Shanaar appears on the pathway, followed by the Two Rough Fellows dragging Loreleen along. She is in a sad way. Her hair is tumbled about ; her clothes are disarranged ; her bodice unbuttoned, and her skirt reefed half-way up, showing a slim leg, with the nylon stocking torn. One of the Rough Fellows is carrying her hat with its cock-like crest in his hand. A blood-stained streak stretches from a corner of an eye half-way down a cheek. Her face is very pale, and intense fright is vividly mirrored in it. She is dragged by the arms along the ground by the men, led by Shanaar, to where the Priest is standing. When she is nicely placed before him, she hangs her head, ashamed of her dishevelled state, and of the way she has been pulled before him. Other men and women follow them in, but are checked from crowding the pathway by an order from the Priest. The Messenger rises from his seat on the wall, and comes near to where the men are*

holding Loreleen. He has placed the carrying straps of his accordion over his shoulders, and now bears the instrument on his back. Michael, the Bellman, and One-eyed Larry, stand some way behind the Priest. Marion and Lorna have started to come to Loreleen's assistance, but have been imperiously waved back by Father Domineer, and have retreated back towards the house, where they stand to stare at what happens. Shanaar stands at the gateway, gloating over the woeful condition of Loreleen.

Father Domineer [*to those following the men dragging in Loreleen*]. Go back ; keep back there ! Give th' honied harlot plenty of space to show herself off in.

Shanaar [*down to Father Domineer*]. Tell her off, Father ; speak to her in th' name of holy Ireland !

Father Domineer [*to Sergeant*]. You go, Sergeant, an' keep them from coming too close ; [*to Shanaar*] an' you, Shanaar, stand at the opposite end to keep any others from pressing in on us. [*To the men holding Loreleen*] Bring her a little closer.

[*The men drag her closer.*

Father Domineer. Now, jerk her to her feet. [*The men jerk her upright.*] Well, me painted paramour, you're not looking quite so gay now ; your impudent confidence has left you to yourself. Your jest with heaven is over, me lass ! [*To the men*] How did you ketch her ?

1st Rough Fellow [*with pride*]. We've been on her tail, Father, for some time. We ketched her in a grand car with a married man ; with a married man, Father, an' he thryin' to put an arm round her.

2nd Rough Fellow [*butting in to share the pride of capture*]. So we hauled her outa th' car, and hustled her here to you.

Lorna [*running over to the man nearest to her, and catching his arm*]. Let th' poor lass go, you cowardly lout ! I know you : your whole nature's a tuft of villainies ! Lust inflames your flimsy eyes whenever a skirt passes you by. If God had given you a tusk, you'd rend asundher every woman of th' disthrict !

Father Domineer [*angrily — to Lorna*]. Get back to your place, woman ! [*Shouting, as she hesitates*] Get back when I tell you !

[*Lorna moves slowly away from Loreleen's side and goes into the house.*

Marion [*as she follows Lorna into the house*]. Dastard knights of Columbanus, do noble work, an' do it well !

Loreleen [*to Father Domineer — appealingly*]. Make them let me go, Father, an' let me get into th' house ! It was Sailor Mahan promised me enough to take me away from here that made me go to him. I shouldn't have gone, but I wanted to get away ; [*brokenly*] get away, away ! Five pounds he gave me, an' they took them off me, with th' last two pounds of me own I had left.

Father Domineer [*savagely*]. Sailor Mahan's a decent, honest soul, woman ! A man fresh for th' faith, full of good works for clergy an' his neighbours. [*He bends down to hiss in her ears*] An' this is th' man, you sinful slut, this is th' man you would pet an' probe into a scarlet sin !

Loreleen. I only wanted to get away. I wanted to get away from Sailor Mahan as much as I wanted to get away from all here.

Father Domineer [*to the two Rough Fellows*]. Where's Sailor Mahan ?

1st Rough Fellow. Th' people pelted him back to his home an' proper wife, Father, an' he's there now, in bed, an' sorry for what he thried to do.

Loreleen [*plaintively*]. Make them give me back th' last few pounds I had.

Father Domineer [*to the Rough Fellows*]. You shouldn't have handled Sailor Mahan so roughly. Where's the money?

2nd Rough Fellow. We tore it up, Father, thinkin' it wasn't fit to be handled be anyone of decent discernment.

Loreleen [*emphatically*]. They didn't; they kept it. [*Stifling a scream*] Oh, they're twisting me arms!

Father Domineer [*cynically*]. Don't be timid of a little twinge of pain, woman, for, afther th' life you've lived, you'll welther in it later. [*To the two Rough Fellows*] Yous should have kept th' money to be given to th' poor.

Messenger [*coming over to the Rough Fellow on Loreleen's right — calmly*]. Let that fair arm go, me man, for, if you don't, there's a live arm here'll twist your neck instead. [*With a shout*] Let it go! [*After a nod from the Priest, the 1st Rough Fellow lets Loreleen's arm go. The Messenger goes quietly round to the 2nd Rough Fellow.*] Let that fair arm go, me man, or another arm may twist your own neck! Let it go! [*The 2nd Rough Fellow sullenly does so.*] Now stand a little away, an' give th' girl room to breathe. [*The two Rough Fellows move a little away from Loreleen.*] Thank you. [*To the Priest*] Now, Father, so full of pity an' loving-kindness, jet out your bitther blessin', an' let th' girl go. An' thry to mingle undherstandin' with your pride, so as to ease th' tangle God has suffered to be flung around us all.

Father Domineer [*fiercely — to the Messenger*]. Keep farther away, you, for th' crowd is angry and their arms are sthrong ! We know you — enemy to th' glow of tradition's thruth, enemy to righteous reprobation, whose rowdy livery is but dyed in rust from th' gates of hell ! [*To Loreleen*] An' you, you'd hook your unholy reputation to a decent man's life. A man, like Sailor Mahan, diligent in his duty, th' echo of whose last prayer can ever be heard when another worshipper enters th' church. You'd sentence him to stand beside you, you shuttle-cock of sin !

Loreleen [*roused to indignation*]. Oh, end it, will you ! You fail in honesty when you won't make them give me back what they robbed from me. When you condemn a fair face, you sneer at God's good handiwork. You are layin' your curse, sir, not upon a sin, but on a joy. Take care a divil doesn't climb up your own cassock into your own belfry !

Father Domineer [*furiously*]. You'll dhribble th' blackness of sin no longer over our virtuous bordhers ! [*He hisses the words out*] Stipendium peccati mors est ! Get away from here quicker than you came, or it's in your coffin you'll be — in your coffin, your coffin !

Shanaar [*from the gateway*]. A merciful sentence, an aysey one, for a one like her !

Loreleen [*half defiantly*]. How am I to go where I'd like to go, when they took all I had off me ? How am I to go for miles with me clothes near rent from me back, an' frail shoes on me feet ?

Father Domineer [*putting his face closer to hers*]. Thrudge it ; thrudge on your two feet ; an' when these burn an' blister, go on your knees ; an' when your knees are broken an' bruised, go on your belly ; crawl in th' dust, as did th' snake in th' Garden of Eden, for dust is th' right cushion for th' like of you ! [*He raises himself erect, and commands in a loud voice*] Go now !

[*Loreleen turns away, goes slowly through the gateway, and along the road outside. As Loreleen reaches the gate, Lorna runs out of the house. She is wearing a dark-red cloak, and carries a green one over her arm. She has a fairly large rucksack strapped on her back.*

Lorna [*calling as she runs out of the house*]. Loreleen ! [*Loreleen halts but does not turn her head.*] Loreleen, I go with you ! [*Lorna shoves Father Domineer aside at the gateway, nearly knocks Shanaar over, and hurries to Loreleen. Draping the green cloak over Loreleen's shoulders*] I go with you, love. I've got a sthrong pair of shoes in the sack you can put on when we're free from th' Priest an' his rabble. Lift up your heart, lass : we go, not towards an evil, but leave an evil behind us !

                              [*They go out slowly together.*

Father Domineer [*taking the Sergeant by the arm*]. Let her go quietly to her own. We'll follow some of the way to prevent anyone from harming her. [*Down to Michael*] Be of good cheer, Michael ; th' demon is conquered — you can live peaceful an' happy in your own home now.

[*He goes out with the Sergeant, followed by all who may be there, except Michael, the Messenger, and Shanaar.*

[*The Messenger goes back to the wall, sits on it sideways, takes the accordion from his back, and begins to play very softly, the air of " Oh, Woman Gracious ". Shanaar leans on the wall from the outside, looking down at*

Michael, who is now seated gloomily on a chair beside the table, an elbow resting on it, his head resting on the hand.

Shanaar [*down to Michael*]. His reverence never spoke a thruer word, Mick, than that of you'd have happiness an' peace now. You were a long time without them, but you have them now.

Michael [*doubtfully*]. Maybe I have, Shanaar, an', God knows, I need them. [*He pauses for a moment, thinking*] I wondher will Lorna come back?

Shanaar [*emphatically*]. Oh, devil a come back! You need have no fear o' that, man. An' fortunate you are, for a woman's always a menace to a man's soul. Woman is th' passionate path to hell!

Messenger [*playing softly on his accordion and singing*] :
    Oh, woman gracious, in golden garments,
    Through life's dark places, all glintin' go ;
    Bring man, in search of th' thruth tremendous,
    Th' joy that ev'ry young lad should know.

    Then come out, darlin', in reckless raiment,
    We'll dance along through Ireland gay,
    An' clip from life life's rich enjoyments,
    An' never want for a word to say.

[*Marion has come into the porch, and now stands at the door, watching the Messenger. She is covered to her knees by a bright-blue cloak.*

    Cling close to youth with your arms enthrancin',
    For youth is restless, an' loth to stay ;
    So take your share of th' kisses goin',
    Ere sly youth, tirin', can slink away !

[*Marion crosses the garden towards the gate, and is about to go through it when the Messenger catches her by the arm.*

Would you leave me here, alone, without a lass to love me ?

Marion [*gently removing the hold of his hand on her arm*].   Your voice is dear to me ; your arm around me near seals me to you ; an' I'd love to have——

Messenger [*quickly*].   Your lips on mine !

Marion.   But not here, Robin Adair, oh, not here ; for a whisper of love in this place bites away some of th' soul !   [*She goes out by the gateway, and along the road taken by Lorna and Loreleen.   The Messenger stays where he is, wistful and still.   Just before she goes*] Come, if you want to, Robin Adair ; stay, if you will.

Shanaar [*to the Messenger*].   Stay, Messenger.   Take a warnin' from a wise oul' man, a very wise oul' one, too.   [*He turns his head to look peeringly to the left along the road*] What's this I see comin' ?   If it isn't Julia, back from Lourdes, an' she on her stretcher still !   I'd best be off, for I've no inclination to thry a chatter with a one who's come back as bad as she was when she went.

[*He bends down nearly double, so as not to be seen, and slyly and quietly steals away.*

[*After a pause, Julia comes in on her stretcher, carried by the two Rough Fellows as before, her father, silent and stony-faced, walking beside her.   The stretcher is laid down in the garden just inside the gate.   Julia is covered with a rug, black as a winter's sky, and its sombre hue is enlivened only by the chalk-white face of the dying girl.   The Messenger has gone from the gateway, and now stands in a half-to-attention, military way, a little distance from the stretcher, looking down at Julia.   Julia's father stands, as before, behind her head. Michael sits, un-noticing, elbow on table, his head resting on his hand.*

Julia [*in a toneless voice — to no-one in particular*]. Lorna, I want Lorna.

Messenger [*gently*]. She's gone, Julia.

Julia. Gone ? Gone where ?

Messenger. To a place where life resembles life more than it does here.

Julia. She's a long way to go, then. It's th' same every-where. In Lourdes as here, with all its crowds an' all its candles. I want Loreleen.

Messenger. She's gone with Lorna, an' Marion's followed them both.

Julia. Then there's no voice left to offer even th' taunting comfort of asking if I feel better.

Messenger. There's Michael Marthraun there.

Julia [*after a long look at Michael*]. He, poor man, is dyin' too. No-one left, an' th' stir there was when I was goin' — th' mayor there, with all his accouthered helpers ; th' band playin' ; Father Domineer spoutin' his blessin' ; an' oul' Shanaar busy sayin' somersaultin' prayers ; because they all thought I would bring a sweet miracle back. [*She pauses.*] There was no miracle, Robin ; she didn't cure me, she didn't cure me, Robin. I've come back, without even a gloamin' thought of hope. [*She pauses again ; with a wan smile*] I can see your whole soul wishin' you could cure me. Touch me with your questionable blessin' before I go.

Messenger [*very softly*]. Be brave.

Julia. Nothin' else, Robin Adair ?

Messenger. Evermore be brave.

Julia [after a pause]. Dad, take me home.

> [*The Rough Fellows take up the stretcher and carry it out, the stony-faced father following in the rear without a word.*

Michael [raising his head from his hand to look at the Messenger]. Maybe Lorna might come back. Maybe I mightn't have been so down on her fancy dhressin'.

Messenger [tonelessly]. Maybe she will ; maybe you mightn't.

Michael [tonelessly too]. It'll be very lonely for me now. All have left me. [*He takes a set of rosary beads from his pocket, and fingers them.*] I've no one left to me but th' Son o' God. [*He notices the Messenger settling the accordion comfortably on his back, and watches him going to the gate.*] Are you goin' too ?

Messenger [shortly]. Ay.

Michael. Where ?

Messenger. To a place where life resembles life more than it does here.

Michael [after a pause]. What, Messenger, would you advise me to do ?

Messenger [turning at the gate to reply]. Die. There is little else left useful for the likes of you to do.

> [*He swings his accordion comfortably before him, and plays a few preliminary notes. Then he starts to sing softly as he goes away along the pathway outside ; while Michael*

leans forward on to the table, and buries his head in his arms.

Messenger [*singing and accompanying himself on the accordion—as he is going off*] :

> She's just like a young star out taking the air —
> Let others be good or be clever —
>
> With Marion gay, a gay flower in her hair,
> Life becomes but a pleasant endeavour.
>
> When building a city or making the hay,
> I'll follow her close as night follows day,
>
> Or lads follow lasses out nutting in May,
> For ever and ever and ever !

THE END

STAR OF THE SEA

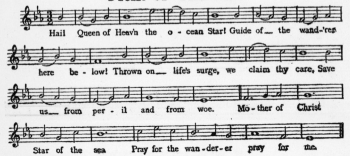

Hail   Queen of Heav'n the   o - cean Star! Guide of — the wand-'rer

here   be - low! Thrown on — life's surge, we   claim thy care, Save

us — from   per - il   and   from   woe.   Mo - ther of   Christ

Star   of the   sea   Pray for the wan-der-er   pray for   me.

WHEN MEN WAS MEN

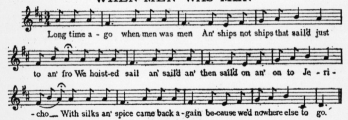

Long time a - go   when men was men   An' ships not ships that sail'd just

to an' fro We hoist-ed sail   an' sail'd an' then sail'd on an' on to Je - ri -

- cho — With silks an' spice came back a-gain be-cause we'd nowhere else to   go.

LORELEEN'S SHANTY

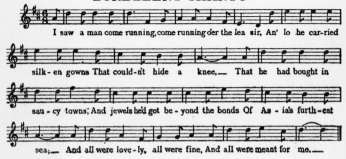

I saw a man come running, come running o'er the lea sir, An' lo he car-ried

silk - en gowns That could-n't hide a   knee, — That he had bought in

sau - cy towns; And jewels he'd got be - yond the bonds Of   As - ia's furth-est

sea; — And all were love-ly, all were fine, And all were meant for me. —

MUSIC FOR COCK'S DANCE

OH WOMAN GRACIOUS

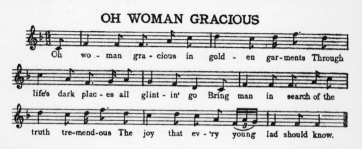

Oh wo - man gra - cious in gold - en gar - ments Through life's dark plac - es all glint - in' go Bring man in search of the truth tre - mend - ous The joy that ev - 'ry young lad should know.

MARION

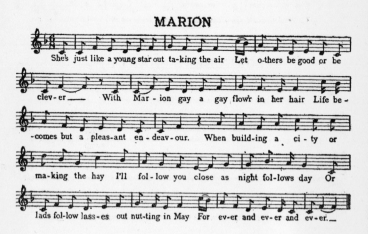

She's just like a young star out ta-king the air Let o-thers be good or be clev - er— With Mar - ion gay a gay flow'r in her hair Life be--comes but a pleas-ant en - deav - our. When build-ing a ci - ty or ma-king the hay I'll fol - low you close as night fol-lows day Or lads fol-low lass-es out nut-ting in May For ev-er and ev-er and ev-er.—

PRINTED BY R. & R. CLARK, LTD., EDINBURGH